EVERYTHING IS SPHERICAL:
an ANTHOLOGY of DYSLEXIC W

It's widely accepted now that dyslexia and creativity have some kind of partnership. But the concept of dyslexics as writers is still new and unexplored. This anthology, authored by dyslexics, aims to bridge this gap. It demonstrates, not only that dyslexics can and do write but also, how the writing of dyslexics complicates and rejuvenates the concept of 'norm'. It offers a reader visual narratives thick with disobedience, subversiveness and thoughts of outsiderness.

Naomi Folb is a researcher, editor and creative writer. She founded RASP, a specialist publishing company for dyslexic writers, whilst completing her PhD on the subject of dyslexia and how dyslexic's shape meaning from their experience. She has published several articles on dyslexia, dyslexic authorship and writing. This is the second anthology of dyslexic writers she has edited.

Sarah Fearn is a Bookseller and dyslexic writer. She graduated from the University of Kent with a degree in English, American Studies and Creative Writing in 2010. She began developing Dysbooks shortly afterwards; an online resource for dyslexic adults with an interest in literature, and for those supporting younger dyslexics to develop a love of reading and writing for pleasure.

EVERYTHING IS SPHERICAL

EVERYTHING IS SPHERICAL:
an ANTHOLOGY of DYSLEXIC WRITERS

Edited By Naomi Folb & Sarah Fearn

Rebelling Against Spelling Press

Everything is Spherical: An Anthology of Dyslexic
Writers

First published in 2014

Book design by Naomi Folb at RASP

ISBN 978-0-9570330-3-0

Published by RASP

11 Thameswalk Apartments

Hester Road

London, SW11 3BG

The work by Robert Glück is reprinted with kind
permission of Tyounyi, Santa Fe, 1990, and At the Public
Library, Vol. 18, #3, 1991, a monthly magazine published
by the Friends of the San Francisco Public Library.

this anthology

is dedicated

to dyslexics

everywhere

CONTENTS

PART 3 THE DYSLEXIC IMAGINATION

PART 4 DYSLEXIC PASSION

FORWARD FOREWORD
Louise Tondeur

When we first had an email conversation about this
book in its current form, neither of us were sure
whether it should be called a *forward* or a *foreword*.
I guess the lexic answer would be "look it up" but
that misses the point. After looking it up, I still
won't really understand one as a right word, in the
same way that - as Rebecca Loncraine expresses
beautifully - I don't know which is left or right.

Or rather I contest the concept of left and right:
I could think about it, but I could also turn around
and left and right would suddenly be different.
Words do that too: they / I / we can turn around
and suddenly, gradually they / I / we are different.

Could it be a forward - a shout of "onward" - in
that it reiterates Ross Cooper's call to action in
'Dysobedience'? Or a foreword in that it's a word
that comes first or says that words are important
and that we reserve the right to use them, play
with them, manipulate them, even though they
have been used against us. But looking at *foreword*
it could also be a cupboard, a chaise longue or a
sausage dog or a row of beach huts (because of the
shape of the word). Perhaps a *foreword* is an excuse
to play with words?

I have to say this, even though I sound like a
BBC public service announcement: if you've been

affected by any of the issues that come up in this book, please know you're not alone. Please contact someone. We'd like to put a hand out to you through the pages of this book. You can grasp it if you want us to pull you up out of somewhere, or you can shake it to say hello, or hold onto it out of solidarity. In other words, what I'd like to say as a *foreword / forward* to the first section in particular is that you have a right to be angry if you were let down by education. I'm not trying to put words in your mouth, neither am I the only person capable of telling you this, of course, but it needs saying.

Would you tell any child that he or she is a failure? Would any feeling human being do that? The position is very clear: we have lost our way if as a society we make it our business to tell children they are failures. Why do I even need to write that previous sentence? If you heard that, or you internalised that, we're here to tell you different. There is another way of looking at the world. There is a way of answering back. In this book you'll find some of our answers.

You know, to reiterate that point, we've lost our way as a society if it has become a cultural idiom to consider the whole of learning and teaching as somehow contextualised by failure. Think about a time someone taught you something brilliant, a time when you had an epiphany moment - or a "burst" of "transcendental realisation" - think about a learning and teaching moment in your life, think of several. Here are some of mine:

The time someone told me to lie on my back and look at the stars in a desert; the time someone told me to mistrust binaries; the time I learnt that only practice makes you a writer; the time I heard an amazing lecture on Toni Morrison's Beloved; the time my history teacher got me to stand up and pretend to be Elizabeth I or someone defending Charles I; the historical figure doesn't matter: I learnt about empathy, I learnt about finding my own voice.

There are plenty of people talking about the positive attributes of dyslexia and other kinds of neurodiverse thinking. Plenty of people are challenging the idea that dyslexia and a writing life are mutually exclusive. In fact, several dyslexic writers, myself included, talk about dyslexia as an important influence on their writing process.

For me, it caused the child-me to write obsessively, rebelliously, in notebooks, in handwriting no-one would have been able to read, just to give the lie to people who think you should write neatly and methodically on the lines. I never understood why that was seen as a virtue. So, almost by accident, I practised. I believe it helps me seek out unusual connections, images and ideas more quickly than someone who likes neat, on the line, handwriting.

There are times when I long to be able to think with linearity and greater clarity, times I wish I could spell, times I wish the word that escapes me hadn't escaped; but that these are all part of the writer in me.

I was really pleased to be asked to write the forward / foreword to this book. The writers, voices and stories represented here are diverse and we write on a diverse range of topics: at turns angry, funny, meandering, thoughtful and direct. Read them and write your own.

EDITOR'S PREFACE
Sarah Fearn

You can read this anthology in any order you want, randomly, or in reverse. Not only is it allowed, it's encouraged. But if you do read it in order, you will come to *Dyslexics on Dyslexia* first. It's where you will find my story, *Webs*. The work here is mostly autobiographical, and I found reading through the pieces here together, one after the other, a very powerful experience.

How often do dyslexics communicate their experiences and views on dyslexia, and writing, via the written word? Especially for other dyslexics? How often do any of us tell these stories?

No that often, partly because of the ignorance around dyslexia, and partly because not many platforms exist for dyslexic people to share such experiences and views. It's harder for dyslexic people to record their personal stories and feelings because the most accessible platform to most non-dyslexics is less accessible to us, the written word, or many of us simply lack confidence is using it.

These personal stories, of the adversity of dyslexia, are important. Particularly in how the trouble doesn't come from dyslexia, but other people's reactions to it. Across all these pieces one thing stands out to me, a desire for, and a lack of, understanding. It is what produces suffering in these pieces, and in many dyslexic people's lives.

I think it's something that should be recorded and remembered, the suffering and triumph of dyslexic people, even as I hope this will change so we are more included in education and society. I think sharing these humanized and personal experiences is important in both letting other dyslexics know they are not alone and in validating their own feelings and journey's, and as a way of educating non-dyslexic people. Especially those who interact with dyslexics, or who are in positions to affect them significantly, such as the parents and teachers of dyslexic people.

These stories explore an important part of our history. These things that happened to real people. Some of those things had to change, including how what happened was regarded. This level of maltreatment shouldn't simply be forgotten, it does all those who have experienced it a disservice and denies society a chance to truly learn from it and to prevent it from happening to others.

The rest of the anthology shows dyslexics in action, spinning stories and creating new worlds and not letting a difficulty with accessing written language define them. It's practicing what the more autobiographical and dyslexia specific pieces discuss.

The later parts of the anthology inform and add context to the first section, as well as the first section informing the fiction and poetry and manifestos, and other delights to be found within these pages. They are telling personal stories and discussing dyslexia, too, but from a different angle; everything is spherical. It all flows back and forth, like the tide coming in and out. The authors are more hidden, but the work speaks for them as writers and dyslexics through the quality of the writing and creativity involved.

The stories that these pieces tell are just as vital, just as important, and I think it is incredibly inspiring and moving to have so many together, side by side, communicating in a way they wouldn't normally be able to. Together they tell a larger story about the dyslexic experience, and about dyslexic writers and writing. It is special, and a privilege to have been a part of drawing them all together and delivering them into your hands.

We deserve a chance at the understanding that so longed for within some of these pieces, and not to be defined by what we struggle with and what we are not, but to be seen as whole people with a mix of strengths and weaknesses. We deserve a chance to add to the narrative on dyslexia that historically has been dominated by (albeit often well meaning) non-dyslexics.

This anthology confronts this imbalance, stares it down, and gives dyslexic people a voice that carries and can be heard. Magnified by the combined strength of all those who have contributed. It gives dyslexic people the platform they need, and makes the written word more approachable for both dyslexic reader and writer.

Our words have value, and they have authority. If you take nothing else away from this anthology, I hope that you at least take a sense of this away with you, of the significance of your own stories, and of your own potential. To know that you are not, and never have been, alone.

INTRODUCTION
Naomi Folb

What are dyslexic writers?

It's widely accepted now that dyslexia and
creativity have some kind of partnership. But the
concept of dyslexics as writers is still new and
unexplored. A mainstream view would hold that
dyslexics, though "creative" and "imaginative",
struggle to write. This is often explained as an
inherent disability or impairment.

This anthology presents a more nuanced view of
dyslexia, authored by dyslexics - many of whom
are published "successful" authors. As a collection,
it reveals that dyslexics both can and do write.
One might also argue that the writing of dyslexics
rejuvenates writing norms through interesting
narrative techniques and obscuring grammatical
conventions.

For whom is this book intended?

This collection is aimed at the dyslexic reader;
one who 'sees' and 'conceptualises' the world

differently from the 'norm'. The reader is imagined to appreciate a visual narrative, and be interested in words, their dimensions, tricks and possibilities.

It is also imagined that a dyslexic reader might identify with the authors depiction of their 'innocence' spoiled by normative ideals and the stories depictions of disobedience, subversion and outsiderness.

While many fonts are heralded as 'better' for a dyslexic reader, we've chosen to print this book in Palatino, which is a beautiful and elegant font, therefore pleasing to the visual thinker. We've also given the text plenty of space with broad margins so as not to crowed the text, and give the dyslexic reader lots of thinking space. As well, the anthology is printed on cream paper and align it left, for a better, cleaner, reading experience.

Key themes in the book

There are five main themes in this book: *dyslexia, rebellion, imagination* and *passion*. While some of the prose and stories could belong in more than one category, and some are only tangentially linked, the themes overlap in many places and from multiple angles and as such, everything is spherical.

The theme of sphere and dimension appear in *Part 1 Dyslexics on Dyslexia*. Here the topic of dyslexia is addressed and the normative ideals about the way one *should* think and learn are questioned and critiqued. It offers a good springboard by which to consider the themes which emerge in the more creative writing which follows.

Part 2 Dyslexics on Rebellion, wrestles the topics of authority, protocol, procedure and customs. All are put under the microscope, while the darker, more sinister side of the dyslexic's imagination, as a response to normativity, prick at reality. The conditions under which the dyslexics thinking is shaped is both envisaged and re-written.

Part 3 The Dyslexic Imagination, is mostly surreal and magical realism. It's conveyance of the world from a different perspective is suffused with experimental narrative techniques. Writing traditions are forged, buried and displaced to re-surface with sharp visual thinking, lustrous grammar and more lone outsider characters.

The closing section, *Part 4 Dyslexic Passion* highlights the dyslexics devotion, dedication and resilience. What is uncovered is the earth of the dyslexic's character; suffering and enthusiasm fused. What emerges is a special kind of persistence and zeal, tingling the surface of the narratives.

Each section is separate, yet unified by the themes of difference and outsiderness. What permeate throughout the anthology calls forth a way of viewing the world, which stand out from the crowd, and disrupt old ways of thinking about dyslexia. Linking us, in a big spherical loop, back to the beginning which re-imagines how dyslexia - and dyslexics - should be viewed in the post-modern era.

How to read this book

Whatever you do, do not read this book linearly, unless you want to. A dyslexic reader must - or may - start by reading something that interests them, and allow their interest to do the navigation.

Read it your own way. Maybe under a tree, on a train, in a forest, or alone in bed with a cup of tea. Read it and daydream if you want, but whatever you do, do not be inhibited by convention.

DYSLEXICS ON DYSLEXIA

EVERYTHING IS SPHERICAL
by Rebecca Loncraine

Do you know the geometry of your own imagination?

My mind cannot, simply cannot, obey the idea
of right and left, the two-sides theory. Politically,
bodily, spatially, my internal three-dimensional
mirror-mind flips everything around, showing
many more than two sides to things, or sometimes
no sides at all, everything being a continuum of
light.

I've tried over many years to obey the unwritten
law of the two halves. I'm constantly being told that
the world and my body can be neatly paired into
"left" and "right", into two distinct hemispheres.

But even the pushers of the two halves theory
acknowledge that no two sides of anything are
exactly equal. All is asymmetry.

I know deep in my blood that there are more
than two sides to every story; I think the structure
of my brain allows me to know this, privileges me
to this insight. Stories, after-all, are as spherical as
everything else. And I don't mean circular.

There's no such thing as a perfect circle.

I find it hard to read the clock-face because 11o'clock and 1, 3o'clock and 9 keep swapping places. Clock-wise and anti-clockwise loop around one another into a latticework instead of two hoops that spin in opposite directions. My mind is thoroughly, promiscuously ambidextrous.

"Are you left-handed?" a woman asks me as I reach for the door handle apparently with my nicely labeled "left" hand. "No" I reply because it seems I write with my "right", although I don't perceive myself as either handed. My hands reach out at random to carry out different tasks in the pool of space that surrounds me.

My mind is a three-dimensional spherical Mobius strip of sorts that perceives the world in multi-coloured shapes that hum and sing out the world and my ever-shifting place in it. The soft pulp of my electric brain experiences everything in terms of many senses that fire simultaneously. Inside my think-feeling mind the senses are all melted together into a waxy landscape without strict border controls, so that to hear is to see, is to feel, is to taste and therefore to know. Mine is a spherical sensory knowing.

What's your knowing like?

I have built inside my mind a memory space ship (and I drew a picture of it) that's a rolling sphere full of cupboards in which I store carefully chosen objects from stories I've read or heard. To recall a story, I enter my round ship of memory, which has no up or down, no left or right, no top or bottom, and open the relevant cupboard to pull out, oh! hear's a nest of cobwebs from Mrs. Haversham's house; here's the axe Raskolnikov murdered his landlady with and here's a puppet from Angela Carter's Toyshop. These flotsam and jetsam objects are emotional triggers back into the stories I took them from.

This giant memory trove spins slowly through the inner solar system of my imagination, and it exerts a gravitational pull towards any new stories I come across in books or in anecdotes told to me by friends. I seize on the shiniest remnants and magpie them into my memory sphere.

I've surrendered to being in the world and in my body in a spherical fashion because I can do nothing else without drowning and disowning myself. But this can make it hard to communicate with others, especially if we're navigating. Some people simply don't believe me when I tell them that the world-theory of right and left makes no sense to me at all; it can seem as though I'm being stubborn and awkward. I try an image of empathy: for me, I explain, trying to slot everything into right and left is like doing extremely long division in your head really quickly. See if you can divide 3,423.6 by 294.7 in a millisecond and you'll know how my head hurts as it spins around on its axis looking for somebody else's dividing line between the left and the right side of anything.

In giving up on the two-sides version of life I feel a sense of guilty shame. An old wound of stupidity flashes past but I also know that in not taking sides, I open myself to the wonder and colour of a world in which I'm undivided from my imagination, unseparated and bewildered into being whole.

WITH DUE RESPECT
by Matthew Scurfield

The Manor Secondary School for boys opened as a
brand new municipal building in 1959, my first year,
with all the hope in the world. Rows of woodwork
and metalwork benches decorated with gleaming
tools waiting patiently for young and eager hands
to go to work. Science laboratories ready for every
experiment one could imagine. Immaculate playing
fields partnered a fully equipped gymnasium,
crying out for the swift of foot to fly. And
classrooms, oh the classrooms, crammed full of
bountiful knowledge and delightful stories; where
calligraphy pens, dirty-blue ink and reams of fresh
paper were given out to wide eyed boys, who sat in
rows of regimented desks, excited at the prospect of
the next abundant lesson.

What a load of old bollocks that turned out to be!

I entered this raw and seething atmosphere
totally unprepared, without any understanding of
the armour and weaponry necessary to survive.

The top class was A, the bottom D and below D
there was Removed, the class where I was to start

my first term. Along with myself there were around twenty other boys who were barely able to speak, let alone read or write. The word failure, began pounding around, a permanent fixture inside my numb skull. *"You're not stupid, Matthew, of course you can read and write!"* The formalities kept telling me otherwise. An academic fiasco, played out against a backdrop of scholastic excellence.

I was raised in a family of collective principles, in post-war Cambridge. My mother and father lead a prominent, bohemian, academic lifestyle. Well-read and, well versed in politics and the arts, they were privately educated and came away from Cambridge University before the war with B.A.s in English literature. A wing of the engineering faculty was named in honour of my maternal forefathers. We lived in a big house with a luxurious garden. My immediate neighbourhood was home to lorded engineers, scientists, grammarians, philosophers, mathematicians, doctors of law, of history, of sociology, of biology, of criminology, in any language, in any colour, in any array; an endless fount of expertise. My mates from school, the ones I wasn't too embarrassed to bring home, called where I lived 'the posh side of the tracks', or 'nob's row'.

After the stock-in-trade misery of Primary School, the combination of my parents' political ideals and flunking a measly exam catapulted me headfirst into the Manor, which was situated on the edge of a council housing estate, in one of the seedier regions of that acclaimed city. Might as well have been on the other side of the moon, for all I knew.

As far as the school authorities were concerned, here was this boy from the posh side of town in the same class as a bunch of oiks. Some teachers seemed perplexed, but most went out of their way to put a son of privilege well and truly out of joint. More like boot camp than a campus of love and learning. Subjects were thrown at us at break neck speed; masters, given licence by the policies of the day, threating us with punishment if we didn't keep up. I found myself constantly lagging behind. And if struggling with schoolwork wasn't enough to reduce me to a quivering wreck, grappling with the enemy certainly was.

It became perfectly normal during a break to see at least one brawl where blood was spilt. Some of the harder boys brandished flick knives, or knuckledusters, particularly if the punch-up took place outside the gates after school. By the time of my second year I'd seen a boy impaled and killed with a javelin, another shot and paralysed with an airgun and many horrific fistfights. If ever the fire of a fight caught up with me, which it increasingly did, I'd become blind with rage and usually wound up beaten into the submission and tears of a snotty, toffee nosed wanker.

This pool of violence, which was my school, came to dictate my way of operating in the world; if it wasn't for learning a lot about how to escape the horrors and how to face up to them, I just wouldn't have survived. Using whatever creative intervention I could muster, I quickly learnt to drop those H's and paint a local accent so as to merge with the other boys. Playing the idiot, buffoon, or total arsehole, as many of us did, became my expertise. By the time I reached my third year, I was thought of as nothing more than a troublemaker. For me and many of my mates, however, it was simply a matter of primitive survival.

"*Now,*" that old familiar voice declares, "*we all have our cross to bear. You wouldn't be where you are today without such tapestry! That's what happens in life. It's called character building!*" Like banging your head against a wall to know how it feels when you stop.

If nothing else, I learnt what it was like to be schooled as an inferior, second-rate citizen. Mine was just one of thousands of schools through which a massive part of the population was filtered and segregated like chaff from wheat. The polite excuse was that there were those who were good with their hands and those who weren't, white-collar or blue-collar workers, dictated by the industrial needs of the day.

Having been branded as innately stupid, we needed to be funnelled and controlled. What better way to do this than to put the fear of god in us. Proverbs 13:24: Whoever spares the rod hates his son, but he who loves him is diligent to discipline him. It's an old story, condoning terror as the main ingredient.

At my primary school the cane was positioned for all to see, like a prized trophy, above a replica of a Van Gogh painting, the one with fishing boats on a beach. This straight red stick was rarely put to task, but it still managed to induce dread into the imagination of a small child. At the Manor it turned out to be a good deal different. Caning was a way of life.

As well as the slipper and the one foot ruler, a lean bendy cane made of rattan was used for dealing out daily doses of punishment at the Manor. Rattan took over from birch, as the preferred instrument of correction, because it was said to have fitted in with Victorian ideals of modesty. Those ideals seemed to stick around for a very long time. Corporal punishment was outlawed in most state run schools as recently as 1986, some twenty seven years after my initiation. It was mainly through conspiratorial talk in the playground that the horrors really flared up. *"Jesus, it really hurts!"* a wide eyed boy would exclaim.

"I put a comic down the seat of my pants, so when the stick hits it don't hurt at all", says another.

"Liar!" snarls his friend

"How many did you get?"

"I got six, burns like a line of fire."

Again and again, these torturous anecdotes kept teasing our deepest fears. If this fiery gossip wasn't enough to push you off your stride, hearing the stick thrashing its soft target through the thin walls of that prefabricated prison certainly did.

We were given a lecture about school image. How the cane would be administered to any boy who stepped out of line. We were told that this diabolical form of control would only be used if it fitted the magnitude of the crime, but we were never told what constituted a crime worthy of such treatment. The deputy headmaster Mr Maxwell, a short, podgy man, whose face frequently looked like it was about to explode, took severe delight in telling the assembled school that even through two or three layers of clothing the cane would impart a considerable sting.

"Of course," he whispered with a hint of secrecy in his voice, *"the pain is even more intense if applied to the bare buttocks"*.

Mr Maxwell had been brought in from my brother's Secondary School, so I had warnings of his heartless reputation. His regime wasn't helped by the fact that he'd brought with him some of the toughest rejects in the shire; teddy boys, motorcycle hoodlums, thugs who'd beat the unsuspecting to a pulp if you so much as looked at them the wrong way. Heeding my brother's advice, for the most part, I managed to avoid Maxwell's hooks. Then, as the terms ground to a painful crawl, I became careless with my behaviour.

"*SCURFIELD, HANSLOW and WELFORD,*" he yelled out our names with vitriolic hatred steaming from his lips,

"*SEE ME AFTER ASSEMBLY!*"

We had been trying to lighten the occasion, no doubt joshing around, whilst the rest of the school was singing the national anthem. To Mr Maxwell this was a red rag to a bull. He hauled us out in front of the whole school and told everyone we would be thrashed for degrading the image of the school and worst of all, for violating the Queen. I was beaten severely. Like my tougher companions, I tried to show indifference, but caved in to the devastation of sobbing uncontrollably in front of this dreadful teacher.

"*Please sir, I'm sorry sir!*"

"*WHAT ARE YOU?*"

"*I'm good for nothing.*"

"*WHAT DID YOU SAY?*"

"*GOOD FOR NOTHING, SIR!*"

"*GOOD! NOW GET OUT OF MY SIGHT!*"

◎

My parents' passion for the arts helped to realise

my skill as an actor and in light of all the mess, they encouraged, nay begged me to be involved in the theatre at any level. Thus I took a step toward the stage, with the fear of not measuring up to the score line slashed indelibly across my buttocks.

The man who ran the Arts Theatre in Cambridge at this time was known as Commander Blackwood. He was a forthright gentleman, who had the air and graces of an old fashioned bank manager, rather than someone who might run such a flamboyant affair. During my third year at the Manor, through my mum's involvement with the theatre at a local level, I got to meet the Commander. Much to my surprise, he agreed to give me a job, as a general dogs-body, for the duration of the school holidays.

I was amazed to be extended proper responsibility by the stage staff, especially by the stage director, who prompted me with humour and respect. I worked my socks off. I guess it's hardly surprising that I learnt a damned sight more than I ever would have given the same amount of time at school.

The other side of getting to know the Arts more intimately was going with my parents to see plays before their London opening. My early memory of these excursions conjures up a feeling of nauseous boredom and a longing for the interval, when I would be offered a glass of branded cola in the cool of the foyer; a treat, because fizzy drinks weren't approved of at home.

At first there were limp musicals like *Salad Days* and *No, No, Nanette* and dreary productions of plays such as *Private Lives* and *Fanny by Gaslight*. This feeling of being dragged to the theatre changed, when dramatists like Arnold Wesker, Harold Pinter and Joan Littlewood began to make their mark. The plays got wiry and even connected with some of my disjointed feelings. I can never forget the power of Ian Holm in *The Homecoming*, Roy Kinnear's humorous turn in *Sparrers Can't Sing*, James Booth's sinister twist in *The Fire Raisers* and other great eye openers. But the highlight, in a kind of caustic tumble, would come from the university itself.

◎

The voices of the packed auditorium quietened, as a slight figure in a bow tie and tails walked across the stage, down to the orchestra pit, to the home of a grand piano. The pianist, looking not unlike a dapper penguin, gave a clipped bow and then turned his back to us. He flipped his tailcoat away from his behind, sat down on the stool and proceeded to play the national anthem.

Such was the social etiquette in those days that standing for the anthem before a play or a film was routine. I knew families who even stood when the nation's tune saw out the end of a day's television. The minute the drum-roll sounded the introduction, from village halls to grand pavilions, we rose to the occasion, no matter what and without question.

And, right on cue, everyone in the theatre got to their feet. There was the usual polite silence, as the audience paid their respects. Then, having finished with the Queen, the house lights dimmed, prompting us back into our seats. Penguin-man went back up onto the stage and walked off, leaving behind the slight shuffling of coats and clearing of throats; familiar sounds from a theatre ready to descend into the world of play. After a naked pause, the well-groomed man came back. And with the same equal poise, he crossed the stage, as before, stepped down to the piano, as before, bowed and flicked his tails, as before, and sat and played our national anthem, as before. Perplexed, if not embarrassed, the audience decided amongst themselves that he must have made a mistake. We dutifully stood up to help him out. With whispers of faux pas sweeping through the theatre, Penguin-man departed for a second time.

Just as the audience began to settle, ready to put this rather peculiar incident behind them, the pianist returned to the stage once again. Repeating the exact same ritual, a little twitchy perhaps, the diminutive figure resumed his place at the piano. And for what seemed like the umpteenth time that evening, he keyed out the anthem. For a few sweet seconds the spectators were gripped in nothing less than opened-mouthed contortion. Some of the more patriotic obliged by getting up from their seats; others remained still and incensed. This was a step too far. Confusion reigned. When it finally sunk in that he was teasing our obedience, gasps of outrage and awkwardness gave way to a wave of elation, laughing and clapping.

Seems tame now, but back then, by a good few miles, this was radical. The breakdown, of our machinelike etiquette, seemed nothing short of a revolution. It blew fresh, vibrant air into what I had expected to be a stuffy night out at the theatre.

The man playing the piano was Dudley Moore. The play was Beyond the Fringe, acclaimed today as pivotal to the birth of satirical theatre. It became a huge irony for me, this show, because of what had happened with Mr Maxwell at The Manor. But the screw that stuck in my throat was: *How come Dudley got away with it and I didn't!?*

I had what is held up as the best within my grasp, but in the end was given the worst of what our schooling gives out to a vast majority – a feeling of disempowerment that comes from being incessantly told what to feel and think. I hovered awhile, like a bird in view of a city of spires, only to crash into a psychotic divide.

I may have come from the opposite end of the social spectrum to the boys I went to school with, but I was labelled and packaged as they were: a slow learner, word-blind, or as I came to embody from playground politics, thick and stupid. These derogatory terms, wrapped around my torso by the mechanism we call school, were measured against my background and mapped out my path in the world.

When my sentence was finally up, I couldn't wait to escape. Along with the rest of the losers I was

systematically chucked out, like a rotten piece of
meat from a butcher's shop. With a pathological
hatred of school, Cambridge and all it represented,
I left when I was fifteen, embroiled in a web of
semi-illiteracy, bitterness and relief. Unsurprisingly,
I veered dangerously close to the abyss.

By the time I hit my twenty-first birthday I'd
lost all confidence in doing anything worthwhile.
Somehow I managed to avoid an untimely death,
by clinging onto the hope that I might find some
respect in the acting profession. Between the drugs,
drink and rock 'n' roll there were intermittent
sessions of therapy and the discovery of yoga. But
it wasn't until I met Steven Berkoff, and started
acting in his company, that I really began to put the
negative image I had of myself to some inventive
use. By kicking the twisted heap of anger I had
accumulated in my life up onto the stage, I was able
to take a monumental leap into new and positive
horizons.

Several decades later, in my early fifties, through
the vagaries of academic fashion and a series of
fateful interventions, I gradually became aware
of the fact that I might be dyslexic. Eventually,
following some months of indecision, I resolved to

get myself tested. For the first time in my life, I flew past the finishing post in an exam and took gold. I was very dyslexic! But the initial euphoria of having a hook to hang my troubled past on soon gave way to a feeling of betrayal and abuse.

Caning becomes a glaring metaphor for an education system that goes to any lengths to get what it wants. Sadly, there are more ways to skin a cat; playing one kid off against another, tearing them down for being useless in front of the class, belittling their intelligence and so on.

In 1729, William Blake wrote about the price we pay, when stultifying a child's love of learning, in his poem *The Schoolboy*.

How shall the summer arise in joy,
Or the summer fruits appear?
Or how shall we gather what griefs destroy,
Or bless the mellowing year,
When the blasts of winter appear?

The sensitivities summed up so eloquently in the last verse of this iconic poem, have been brushed aside as impossible, or at best simplified ideology, for so long. Taking a feather from the great man's cap, I see how much time I wasted, pulling away from the child's heart.

Being beaten for my sins was obviously inexcusable. But, as horrendous as this abuse certainly was, being judged a no-hoper left the greatest scar.

Imagine if I'd been able to ask a friend how to spell a certain word, without shame; get the teacher to slow down when giving dictation, without shame; ask the shopkeeper to fill in the cheque for me, without shame; get help with the tax form and the utility bill, without shame. Imagine the joy in tackling that illusive, lexical, exercise, without dread and frustration. I believe this would have been possible, years ago, if I hadn't been punished for being dyslexic.

Since the word dyslexia wasn't part of the school vocabulary in my day, there can be no doubt that measuring myself against the almighty scholastic yardstick caused immeasurable damage. Which leads me to wonder what others less fortunate than I might inflict, on themselves and the world, if they aren't able to realise and celebrate their learning difference?

Disobedient or not, it doesn't make sense to

chop myself in to pieces, and then spend the short time I have left favouring, or avoiding, one piece over another. Aside from that lifelong struggle with shame, I now believe passionately that rather than being a part, a side, or indeed anything to be ashamed of, dyslexia stands out as an integral and important asset. I'm convinced that thinking visually, spatially, or, if you need one of the labels, being dyslexic, saved me from a life of mediocrity and made seemingly impossible tasks possible.

DYSOBEDIENCE
by Ross Cooper

To be dyslexic is to dysobey. Not as defiance, but because we must. Dysobedience begins as unintentional 'disobedience'.

From an early age we are surrounded by people who do not understand who we are. They expect us to be no different from them, and therefore different from who we are. So they start to suspect that there must be something wrong with us, or as my aunty wearily used to say, "Ee, you're a funny lad!"

The chastisement for our dysobedience seems to them to be deserved when we 'act' unexpectedly. *What else is the perceived 'laziness', the being 'lost' in dreams and 'forgetting' time but 'disobedience'? Don't we all dislike having to keep tidy and organised and work hard at our rather boring lessons? What's so different about us that we cannot manage it? It must be 'wilfulness', mustn't it?* Later, they resort to thinking of us as 'disabled', when it is they who disable us.

It becomes such a ritualised part of our lives to be humiliated and abused by loved ones and significant others, who seem to think that we have nothing better to do than make their lives difficult, that it comes to define who we are, and who we are not. Our early world revolves around this balance between escape and humiliation; our 'inadequacies', and sometimes our secret worlds, are laid painfully bare for all to see.

This is the seedbed of some early sedition and later self-destruction. Trying to be 'good' inevitably ends in failure, so why not? If we cannot succeed fairly perhaps we can succeed by stealth? Knowing which side your bread is buttered becomes a survival strategy. Remembering where the knife is hidden is altogether more difficult. Becoming emotionally feral, to seek out crumbs of love and comfort through hidden passageways is a dangerous game. Some end in high risk drug taking; the *look at me* as I self-destruct charmers. Some of us are desperate enough to take such gambles. The prisons overflow, and many of us fall by the wayside.

Meanwhile, our masters seek to impose order on the world by categorising it, imprisoning us by drawing lines between 'subjects', 'levels', and indeed people. But unless the categories are based on the substance of underlying structures they simply mislead and control; a form of divide and rule, squeezing the humanity out of all of us.

In contrast dyslexic thinkers seek to understand the complexity of the world by seeing through it to these underlying structures that make the world whole. Like complex, fractal crystal formations blossoming from simple molecular geometries, or rivers snaking forever downwards on the back of gravity until they gorge themselves on the tidal seas. The world does not fit into the categorical boxes any more than we do. The beauty of it is in seeing the connections, the patterns, the spiralling circularity. *Is this not the same with human beings? Yet we are forever told that we can't study B before we have studied A; that we can't study at a 'higher level' before we have accomplished a 'lower'?* Yet these are arbitrary marks in the sand that the tide will inevitably wash away. The idea that ideas and analysis are more difficult than remembering arbitrary information enshrined in historically bizarre literacy is ridiculous. Yet we are constrained and judged by these markers, forever the square pegs in round holes that occasionally surprise them with our insights. Has

it not occurred to them that these are not chance
events, but project like holograms from our way of
thinking; of seeking out underlying structures and
patterns? It is clearly puzzling to linear thinkers,
because they are stuck on the logic of the page
instead of lifting off it and coming round the back of
the symbolic world.

Our holistic thinking manipulates meaning and
discovery through passionate interest and the
making of meaningful connections, rather than
simply ticking someone else's boxes. *What is so
wrong with that? Why are others so intolerant of us?*

There comes a point, if we are lucky enough
to have gained sufficient purchase on the world,
that we realise we are being held back, and our
dysobedience then becomes a strategic imperative.

It is essential to us to cross their boundaries and
firewalls, to make the necessary connections that
bring meaning to otherwise disparate information.
We challenge their divisions at every turn. Yet
in this lies some salvation if we can survive the
dismissive jeers and caustic comments. Seeing
connections across silos of information, bathing
in the kaleidoscope of visual thoughts, exquisite
patterns emerge and surprise us, unscathed by

presupposition. Thinking is a sensory delight; a passionate consummation of swirling colour, curious missing-links in the patterns, sharp relocations in space and the tingle of knowing that the pattern as solution will burst into life. Yet they seek to interrupt this with corrections to our spelling and with unhelpful scaffolding of memorised prompts and old ideas. It doesn't wash! It will not do! You don't fatten a pig by weighing it, you don't fall in love by reading about it, you can't become whole by dismembering the world.

In this context dysobedience is a right, a necessity. While they wish to insist that we remediate our 'deficit' memory and sequential shortcomings, we insist on the entitlement to breathe unsterilized air, to ignore their boundaries, to take risks, to challenge their priorities, in order to remake ourselves whole; to remake no less than the broken and divided world.

◎

Let me rephrase this. We make sense of information by seeing the pattern of interconnections; patterns are meaning. The patterns represent an underlying structure of connections and interactions and priorities in these interactions, that are more complex and subtle and kinetic than simple 'cause and effect'. When presented with an experience, or a series of discrete bits of information, we seek to make it whole. We relate it back to what we know, we turn it around in our visual inner space until the pattern falls into place and then spin metaphors from it to let others see what we can see. We ask 'what if' questions that may reframe everything we 'know'. We seek an overview of everything.

When presented with an experience, or a series of discrete bits of information, we seek to make it whole.

In this sense, we really are little einsteins of everyday phenomena and experience. This means that we may jump to conclusions, or make intuitive leaps of faith. We play with the information. We are less concerned with the details than the important connections and the priorities they represent or articulate. *We wish those that lecture would get to the point! We demand to interact with the information; to learn by doing, not by being told.*

Internally, the feeling that a solution to a problem is emerging into the light is intensely pleasurable and forewarns us that we will know what the solution is, before we understand it or could articulate it; a pre-orgasmic tingle. This process is difficult to put into words, but we learn in bursts, in moments of transcendental realisation (while spending most of our 'education' bored to tears). How can I express this process adequately in words when they play so little part in the process? When you think in swirls of colour and feelings, words can be hard to find.

◉

Let me rephrase this again. It means that we have to actively dysobey the rules of 'learning' provided by those who have power over us.

If we wish to learn to become who we are and make a valid contribution, we must follow the connections where they lead us even when this ignores boundaries between 'subjects', 'levels' and people. It makes us vulnerable to censor, ridicule and humiliation, but it leads to better ideas and new paradigms. It also questions and challenges received wisdom, and sometimes the legitimacy of the higher status of the 'teacher' compared to the 'taught'. Such acts of dysobedience are intrinsic to our success. We either become actively challenging, or passively fail. Most of us are metaphorically beaten into submission and resort to symbolic acts of defiance at best, populating both our prisons and the comedy circuits.

So some of us become leaders in the fields of comedy, acting, art, writing, politics, entrepreneurial business, sport, film making, cooking, journalism, photography and new paradigms and ideas. It is becoming undeniable that the world needs us to save it from itself. But you will notice that most of these achievements do not require 'exam success', or if they did we would disappear from the roll-call of achievers, along with most of the achievements.

Can you imagine such an impoverished world? Exams disable us as surely as breaking our legs, and they hold in place unsustainable models of 'teaching to the test' that impoverish the experience of 'learning' for everyone. We watch in dismay as others 'pass' exams without understanding any of it, while we need to understand before we could remember any of what is required. And all the while we are systematically denied the opportunity to understand. It disgusts me that the academic world remains so divided, so shallow, so hollow, and yet so jealousy guarded against alternatives.

Is it not time to move from dysobedience to social action? If we, as an actively dysobedient group, cannot change the world, I find it hard to imagine anyone else being capable of it. The emotional violence gathered against us already feels insufferable, so what have we got to lose? I lose patience with patience; dysobedience is an inevitable consequence of who we are in an absurd world. Dysobedience is our birth right. It's no longer just about our own survival; it's about us all.

Dysobedience is good.

WEBS
by Sarah Fearn

I pull aside the curtain and turn on the shower. I'm embraced by warm water. My feet burn with the sudden temperature change. I hadn't realised I was so cold.

Jesus I think, *Jesus this is good.*

My ears feel strange and I realise I'm still wearing my studs. I take them out and open the curtain slightly. I throw them, aiming for the bathmat. They roll like dice. One skitters onto the tiles and lands the wrong way up. I look at it for a moment, wondering what it means.

This is stupid, it doesn't mean anything. It's that time of night though, when there is nothing to do and it's too early to go to bed. I can hear the wind toying with the trees and the rain hitting the window; it's out of time with the water hitting my body.

There are no cars on the road outside. I imagine opening the front door and looking down on the town again. There are only lights, white and orange, glowing in the darkness.

Everyone is inside, cosy and safe. They sit
in front of TVs at home, or maybe in a pub
surrounded by warm chatter.

It is one of *those* nights. The nights where I feel...
suspended. There is something waiting inside me
and it feels as if anything, anything can happen.

Stupid. Nothing ever does happen, for all the
magic I feel in the air. There is left over life waiting
to be made into something new, and I'm not brave
enough to try and use it. Instead I cocoon myself in
my ground floor flat, looking for signs in the fall of
an earring.

◎

The water runs off me in strange ways. I play with
it, making channels with my arms. I don't put in
the shampoo yet, this isn't about being clean. No,
this is my time, a chance to think all the things that
go un-thought during the day.

I had tried to read instead. I'd sat down in
my old wicker chair with the floral cushion, and
opened a book of ghost stories.

My mother told me ghost stories on winter nights, when the moon was full, or a sliver as sharp as a claw. She told them to me during thunderstorms and when the air felt like it had lots of little mouths, waiting to attack unprotected flesh.

Those nights were close, so I'd picked the book up and told myself nothing else would do.

I'd read the first story. It was good, but I didn't have the strength for another. I just wasn't in the mood to read, and the TV would be too loud. I gave up and went to hide in the bathroom.

◎

I spot a spider on a white tile level with my face. I don't move. The spider is pawing at the tile with its front legs. There is something wrong with them. They are white with black joints. They look like glass beads, and remind me of a necklace I was given as a child. I can't decide what the problem is, then I spot it. There are six legs instead of eight. Poor thing. Six legs, and it's trying so hard to hold on.

My head throbs. I touch my cheek and imagine

it purple again. Just a headache, I tell myself. Yet I can't stop now. I'm in my mother's car. I won't talk to her. My boyfriend is sitting in the back and he's telling her what happened.

We are the only car on the road. The street lights crash into me in orange waves. I try and breathe normally. *Jesus* I think, and flip down the sunshield. It has a mirror built into it. A face looks back at me.

One side is swollen and bruised. The eye lids are puffy and red. *Jesus, oh Jesus. This can't be my face.*

◎

When I was in primary school I would spend ten minutes or more just examining my refection. I would try to imagine what I would look like when I grew up. I never saw this, not even in nightmares.

The spider slips and I move back. It swings on a thread and reels desperately. I want to help it but I'm worried I will knock it into the bottom of the shower and it will be washed down the drain.

I imagine the water closing over me and being sucked into the darkness, my limbs ripped off by the current.

I shiver, and will the spider to find a better foot hold.

I think about Dolly Parton. In the story I read, the ghost story, Dolly Parton is playing on the radio. We had been talking about her in the car this morning. I was coming back from my brother's 18th birthday party.

"Your dad was telling your aunt Nicola how you had no ambition again," my mother said. She was at the wheel, acting as chauffeur. I groaned. By ambition he meant desire to get a job he approved of, rather than trying to become a writer.

"It's ok, mum said "I told her he was talking rubbish, I told her how well you're doing."

She paused to shift lanes. "You know Dolly Parton? Well she was so poor her mother made her a coat out of rags. She wrote a song about it. She worked really hard and became this big star. Well she said her mother always stuck by her and told her to hold onto her dreams."

I wasn't sure where she was going with this, so I nodded.

"I believe that honey, if you work hard and believe in yourself you can do anything." She set her jaw, she really meant it. I thought of all the people who believed in themselves and didn't succeed.

"Your dad loves you, but sometimes you have to ignore people. You remember when you were small and your teachers, they said you'd never read or write?"

I did. Of course I did. I could still see the old women sitting at a table in the school library like a jury, telling my mother I would never be good at anything. They made my life hell for five years.

I used to dream that I would send them all a letter one day, telling them I had become successful, despite everything they did or didn't do. They would have nothing, and sit alone, looking at this letter and regretting every snide remark or of act of obstinacy.

That was until I met one of them in a bank. I told her I got an A* for my English course work. I expected her face to screw up, and for her to mumble excuses. She smiled instead. She was proud.

I started thinking of a different sort of revenge then, a revenge just for me. I didn't want to hurt anyone, or mar my success with bitterness.

I thought of writing books, becoming an author. *What better revenge of a dyslexic girl against those who got in her way? What better proof of my skill with words?*

My mother was still talking, but I knew this story, about dyslexia lessons and dragging me out from under the bed so I would go to school.

"Look at you now though! Studying a degree in English...you'll be the first in the family to graduate from university. We are all so proud of you."

I close my eyes. What a myth to live up to, dyslexic girl completes English degree. Dyslexic girl is the first in her family to go to university.

She was right, though. I had dreams and I worked for them. I came from a dark place and I had clawed my way out slowly. It felt like all the other kids had started higher up the mountain and had been given crampons. I just had my hands and feet. It hurt like hell sometimes, but I remembered how it felt to be in the dark place, and I held on. I kept climbing.

Nothing is coming out of the shampoo bottle. I

keep shaking it. Eventually it gives in and a syrupy liquid appears in my palm. It smells like coconuts.

The spider finds the grouting, which is easier to grip onto. I watch it climb away and think about webs, in time and relationships.

I think about slipping on the wet tiles.

◎

They were throwing stones at our window. I was living in a house then, a three bed semi. My boyfriend was getting upset, pacing from the window to the door. It had been going on for fifteen minutes and I was sick of his reaction as much as the stone throwing.

"How old are they?" I asked.

"Twelve, maybe thirteen," he said, peeking behind the curtains.

I put my shoes on.

"Well, I'm not being intimidated by children." He held my arm, I glared. I wasn't some princess who needed looking after. I could, would, do what I wanted. He let go.

"You'll be cold," he pleaded. I took my coat from

the hat stand and kissed him. That was all.

◎

They weren't just twelve year olds and they didn't like me going outside. I was pinned against a car, the buckle on my coat hanging at my side, and scraping against the paint as they hit me. It happened too quickly for me to do anything, hit back or even cry out. They were hitting me, and then I heard my boyfriend.

He roared. He had a voice for roaring, deep and gravelly.

"What the hell do you think you're doing?" He sounded bigger than he was. He's 6ft with broad shoulders. It's hard to find shirts that fit him properly. He sounded huge.

My attackers backed off, teenagers in hoodies and dark coats. I was relieved. Then I thought of my boyfriend, of them hurting him, and I wanted him to stop being my white knight. I wanted him to go inside and call the police.

He stood in front of me and stared them down. They were scared of him, the people that hit me. I could see it in their overly shadowed faces.

"I think you'd better go," he said firmly. He took my arm and pulled me back towards the house. I heard them running away behind us.

I was angry then. I didn't run, I refused to run.

"Get me a phone," I shouted, "get me a phone. I'm calling the police." He locked the front door and followed me into the kitchen.

◎

I sat in the car looking at my face. It wasn't part of the story I was writing for myself. This sort of thing didn't happen to me.

I sat in the waiting room of the counsellors, signing a data protection form. I thought this isn't what I planned. *I write about this happening to other people, ones with interesting lives.* I wasn't interesting.

I was slipping, and I could feel the darkness closing over me again.

The spider puts it leg in its mouth and I realise it's drinking. I have never seen a spider do this before. I just assumed they got all their fluids from flies.

I wash out the last of the shampoo and watch the spider clamber awkwardly into a corner. It preens for a moment, wiping its fangs and the top of its head. Then it settles down to watch me, a graceless pink blob.

◎

I get out of the shower, turn it off, towel down and walk naked into the living room. My boyfriend is sitting at a desk with his back to me. He is playing computer games. He glances up.

"You ok?" he mutters, busy killing things.

I love him.

I open the front door and stand on the drive way in the rain. It seems to wake something in me.

"You ok baby?" my boyfriend says. He sounds worried. I smile, of course I'm ok. I am so full of possibility.

WORLD
by Robert Glück

I was dyslectic *avant la lettre* and badly needed glasses as well, so my first four school years were passed minute-by-minute in a fog of real time and the fragment. From a psychological perspective, the humiliation of this long period fuels my attempt (at least in some of my writing) to use language to render the world in a spherical way, to experience the thrill of being entirely awake, risen, the thrill of bringing the world to a point when/ where all secrets are known--which involves, in fact, some further, exponential learning to read.

to use language to render the world in a spherical way

The goal of clarity contains in some measure the goal of sympathetic magic. But the goal contains its own contrary, because the attempt reveals the impossibility of clarity, the parameters of my own faith, and the resistance of language. Therefore, an interesting goal.

◎

I was the last person in the third reading group,

sometimes trading places with a retarded boy. We took turns reading aloud. During my turn I came to a word that looked familiar because of its shape and the letters I knew: w on one side, ld on the other: would. Would also contained u, a letter I didn't know. But where the stranger should have been, there was an r, an acquaintance.

I lived briefly but intensely inside this Martian word. I stalled for a while, but the direction of the hateful sentence (whose entire meaning I'd lost, whose context I'd lost) was forward. I'd like to confuse the thematics of this drama by adding that I was taught in Hebrew school to kiss a book containing the name of God if I dropped the book on the ground (what book didn't contain God's name, how would I know either way?) and this perversity of my forefathers appealed to me. So I said would, but hopelessly threw into the center of the word the sound of the r. To my total astonishment, Mrs. Banks strode across the circle and shook my hand so energetically I almost lost my balance. Then she slapped my back as though I'd made a great advance. I accepted the commotion--what choice did I have? I remained in the dark for a long time about the world I'd discovered, and why making an r sound produced wild joy and affirmation. Misplaced joy.

☉

  I am grateful for the fragment; unity is a disease of meaning. At the same time literature that purveys disjunction generates its opposite, frames itself with a cannon of criticism--authoritative, technical, "closed." This critical theory dictates the meaning of form, the meaning of freedom--that is, it argues a self, even a non-self, which is the reader, which the reader recognizes and agrees to. Maybe we can't avoid unity or disjunction, maybe they enjoy a principle of conservation. In any case, this is my response to Tyonyi's question: *what patterns are influencing habits of reading within poetry?*

☉

  I have remained an extremely slow reader, dazzled, easily lead off the page in forward momentums different from those the author might be choosing; my own work is discursive, at the same time it follows thematic organizations almost decorative in their strict patterns.

I just finished reading Philip Aries' *Hour of Our Death*, a history of death since antiquity, a beautiful book which helps me write about AIDS. I am reading *Crossouts*, Lydia Davis's translation of the second volume of Michel Leiris's autobiography-- marveling how the endless unraveling of interior life at a certain point becomes objective--in that sense "unoriginal"-- without rejecting personal disclosure, loose association and idle speculation which at any point he is free to disown. He organized the book around particular misreadings and misunderstandings.

DELUSIONS OF ADEQUACY
by Eric R. Williams

Stage left: A teachers desk with rolling desk-chair
Center stage: Fifteen student chairs and desks
Stage right: A standing blackboard angled toward the
audiance. An actor walks out and addresses the empty
classroom as if it were occupied.

I might be making this up. It is entirely possible
that I am just a lazy person, and the dyslexia is
an excuse, a con, an elaborate scam to get out of
the good hard work that made this country great.
Maybe I've just been faking it all this time.

Maybe if I had just applied myself and tried a
little harder school wouldn't have been so bad and
You wouldn't have had to do all of the things that
You did. Maybe it's all my fault. Maybe.

The alternative is unthinkable. The alternative is
that you failed. Year after year, school after school,
class after class. Over two thousand days. Did you
hear that teachers?

You wasted over two thousand of my days!
Unsatisfactory. And so You have been held back so

you can learn to be more responsible. That's why you're all here instead of out playing with the other teachers. Not living up to you're potential. I've heard all of your griping.

"We don't get any respect." "It's not fair that we have the worst car in the parking lot" "Its hard to get through to kids these days." "It's is tough to work all day, and grade papers all night."

Well, excuses may work with your parents, but not in the real world. Besides, who ever said life was fair? Now Teachers! You may not remember me but I sure in the hell remember you, each and every one. I listened to you for twelve years now it's your turn to listen to me. Get your butts down behind those little kidney shaped, plywood desks with the bright plastic seats, grab a number two pencil and strap your selves in. Were going for a little stroll down memory lane. We will call this class.

The actor walks to the blackboard and writes the words down with a flourish: The History of Eric Williams 101.

Don't talk; don't fidget, don't you even move! You, what are you raising your hand for? Oh, you have to go to the bathroom? Well hold it! Open your books to page one and prepare for a pop quiz. And for once try to keep your eyes on your own papers. Hey! Quit crying. This is easy. If you have any questions, just ask me. I know the answers.

Our Pop quiz topic of the day is *Dyslexia.*

Question One: Dyslexics think backwards? True or False?

Anyone that said True looses a half-hour recess. Of course we don't think backwards the only idiot that thinks backwards is the one who started that rumor.

Question Two: Dyslexics can be cured by use of special glasses. True or False?

Who said true, raise your hands. OK extra homework for you for the rest of the week. The fact that some ophthalmologist with a little too much testosterone on his hands decided that he could FIX us is beyond embarrassing. What next? Are they going to cure left handed people with a special shampoo? How about arch supports for

Autists?

Question Three: (this is an easy one) Dyslexia is a learning disability. True or False?

Who said True? All of you! Very well, you leave me no choice, you will receive cold leftover tuna casserole in the cafeteria every day this week. Dyslexia is an Ability. Let me repeat it so you slow average folks can understand. Dyslexia is AN ABILITY. Ever hear of Albert Einstein? Leonardo da Vinci? Thomas Edison? Do the names Winston Churchill or Walt Disney ring an Alexander Graham Bell?

These famous people didn't work their magic despite their dyslexia, but because of it. Show me an F student with Dyslexia and I'll show you a girl who can take a car engine apart in the dark, or a boy who can sculpt by looking at the stone and picturing the sculpture before ever picking up the chisel. Your flunky that sleeps through class can probably read a novel a day or remember every item in a room they were in once years ago. Film directors, CEOs of companies, Generals, artists, leaders, dyslexics. The learning ability to flip and manipulate images only becomes a disability when it's up against a rigid system like yours. Your agonizingly slow method of rote memory, and unattached symbol copying turns some of our finest minds into sloth-zombies with low self-esteem. The worst part is that by the time you lot are through with them they have to spend a lifetime unlearning the one lesson that you taught well, that they're stupid or slow or somehow less than.

The pop quiz is over. You all failed. Your parents will receive a note.

DYSOBIDIANT
by Lennie Varvarides

I never do as i am told because i can't recall the
sentence
People speak to fast and while i run though their
worlds to catch up.
I following the wrong signs, arrows pointing in
diagonal postions.
I seem them bright. Leadinging me astray.

Following cats that are chasing rabbits down the whole. Following cats that are chasing rabbits down the
whole. I've gone again.

But I'm not a bad child, Im just boared when you
speak.
You have lost me in your rules.
Your 'dos'
and your 'donts'
and your 'not nows'
and your 'sit downs'
and your 'no you cannot go to the toilet now'

Now I see how riules were ment to be broken.
To be broken and then covered up with lies.
Good well crafted lies. So good that no one can tell

or good enought to make others lie along with you

ಲ

In liying as in sleep there is no stopping.
Freedome is unknowing.
Uncensored.
Dirty.
Like Love ourt to be.

THE DYSLEXIC TERRORIST
by Alex Nile

Imagine the opening scene to the play or film *Oliver Twist*. You see the workhouse, and the thin starving boys stopping their work, being arranged into lines and marching to the kitchen area with their bowls to get some unappealing porridge and a lump of stale bread. The boys are nameless, faceless, and quiet. They are the unknown children - some big, some small, but all unknown and characterless.

The Obedient Dyslexic

The above snippet of *Oliver Twist* describes nameless, faceless, and quiet children. They are obedient in everyway to the rules that are placed on them. Mr Bumble wears a rich blue coat, compared to the boy's shabby grey cloth clothes. He is the rule maker, who lords over them, requiring them to tremble at his name and voice.

Obedience requires rules, it requires you to know your place in society and never stick out. Never *rock the boat*, otherwise society might crumble! The boys in *Oliver Twist* are helpless, they only know the rules that affect them and they were satisfied by working in the Victorian workhouse.

Growing up as a boy with dyslexia I knew I was unlike my two siblings who were doing well at school and getting the praise of teachers and my parents alike. I saw them as normal. They, with my parents, were the majority in my family. Those that enjoyed reading, with the ability to write and spell, those who weren't clumsy or forgot everything they were told within seconds, and those who could tie their shoelaces and school ties with ease.

Me, who was I? At school I was on the slow table, the table that sat in silence. The table that was never called upon to do fun things in class. The ones that were alienated in the playground and had no friends. I was the unseen, unloved and uncared-for one, just like the faceless boys in Oliver Twist. I knew my place, and knew there was no way out for me. I was told I was thick and stupid, and I believed it. I was helpless and often tried to run away from home, as I knew I didn't fit in, I even thought I might have been adopted, like the ugly duckling.

In the Victorian era, with echoes that carried on until only recently. Many middle-class families' hiding children of difference, be it learning, physical, and hearing disabilities, or even mental illness. They would send them away to live in the country, or by the sea for their health, or live out their days in mental institutions. In reality they were moving them away so the rest of the family could live the perception of being normal, without abnormality. These children would never be mentioned in polite company and would live out their days estranged. Examples can even be seen in the UK royal/aristocrat families of such a tradition. These confirm the *obedient* model of disability.

Different from the old saying about children, to be *seen not heard*. In this case it was *to not be seen and not even spoken about*. The underlying rule was: you are abnormal and should fade away unseen and silently.

Some parents of dyslexics unwittingly support such a view. Many dyslexic associations were created by parents. It was almost like they had taken over their child's fight (in some cases they were adult dyslexic children). These parents knew the rules; they knew how society and the system worked, so they took on the fight. But what did this also say, that dyslexics can't advocate for themselves. That they will always be children (even as adults), that their parents will always care for them. Doesn't this reinforce the obedient dyslexic theory that they need others to speak for them, as they are helpless!

The Disobedient Dyslexic

Relating back to *Oliver Twist*, Oliver was forced to be different. He took part in the boy's game to be normal, to fit in – never thinking he might be the one caught out. He was one of the smallest boys; he was weak and small, not a likely rebel, not even the one best suited to the task at hand. But he was chosen by a lottery, the one with the longest straw.

Carefully he went up to get more porridge. His voice begins small but them increases, *"please sir may I have some more"*. The shock of this belligerent child was too much for the adult serving, that

Oliver needed to repeat his request. *"More"*, came the disbelieving reply, and we all know what happens next. The rebellion needed to be quashed without delay otherwise all hell would let loose. The class-order rules needed to be maintained at all costs!

Oliver did not set out to be disobedient, but quickly grew into the role. He enjoyed the increased freedom and didn't so much mind the hardships that came with it. Life was more exciting!

I began to be a disobedient dyslexic child when I found a voice; I finally found something I was good at (art). Till that point I blended in, often for my own safety and easy life, but I also knew I didn't have the chance to be the popular or smart one. 'Popular and smart' seemed to go together in my school. I was always *'the odd one'*, *'the thick one'*!

With my new voice I could show who I was, my personality, rather than the boy that no one really wanted to be friends with, the one who wasn't cool to be seen with, the one you weren't sure if you would get thick if you talked too much to.

So I had a voice, but what was I to do with it. I began to say no to being the silent disabled type. I made myself different (and eccentric) as many dyslexics choose to be. I rebelled against a label that was unhelpful to me. I began to be spoken about, in a good way by my parents. I began to be noticed as someone with special talents. I even began to be noticed for breaking the rules at school, of course the small ones at first, then the bigger ones. Till I was seen as being close to that 'normal' label that everyone else had

To me disobedience is being normal. Knowing the rules, but breaking them.

Not being the dyslexic or the learning disabled label, but more a 'different' label. I don't mind being different. It defines me, and it defines others as being boring.

My two siblings are accountants, I find this boring, boring, boring. They show no or little creativity in their life. In fact they are the obedient ones, the ones that play it safe, and the ones that play it according to the rules.

Me, I'm different, like the child that won't sit down all the time, the one that breaks the cardinal rule of only taking two biscuits as a child when you go out to tea to family/friends of your parents. The one that won't have a normal family – I have two sets of twins! The one that can juggle four careers together (writer, teacher, researcher, and a designer). The one that is unwilling to be defined by society's rules - the disobedient one!

The Subvergent Dyslexic (to contradict the established order)

Returning to *Oliver Twist* theme, which characters could be deemed as subvergent? Could it be Mr Bumble, the manager of the workhouse, who tries to marry the cook and get rich by selling Oliver's mothers pendant, then becoming a gentleman? Could it be Oliver himself who redefines himself from a lowly workhouse boy, or a boy leading funerals, or a thief, to a gentleman's son? Or could it be Fagin, who has set up a refuge for poor children, giving them a trade, a roof over their heads and a future away from poverty, and then amassing riches for his retirement to settle down as a gentleman? Which one of these is the subvergent - to change or destroy the rules?

I would say that both Oliver and Fagin are subvergent. Oliver as a minor is easily plied like clay into so many roles that one can't believe how easily he fits into them. Fagin on the other hand is a dreamer; he aims to settle down as a gent but knows he won't easily accomplish his dream. He wants to change society's rules that say only a man of education or breeding can be a gentleman. He wants to change such rules but deep down he knows the rules are too great for him, so he escapes by dancing and acting the lordly gentleman in private with his jewels.

Thus Oliver is the only one with the ability and skill to be truly subvergent. He is unwilling to play by the rules; he is unwilling to be defined by a single career track. I like other dyslexics, see ourselves as Oliver. Unwilling to be known as a single label e.g. accountant, lawyer etc. Unwilling to take the easy option. Unwilling to fit into the mould of society.

We are the subvergent ones, to not only break the rules, but to change them. To rip up the rulebook. To change society's notion of what a disabled person should be or do for a living. We are the dyslexic terrorists, who will shock and shake society's perceptions of disability. Society relies on labels, to stereotype groups to act in a certain way. Without such labels society is lost, there is chaos!

The social model of disability aims to do this. It aims to see everyone as different, each with the chance to mould society. Each person, no matter how 'different' they are, has a place in society: a right to work, to play, to have a family, and to be 'themselves'. It's a great model but one that shakes society to be bone and aims to rebuild it again. Is it a dream or a possibility?

The path to subvergence is long and sometimes painful, but it's worthwhile and much needed. Not so much for us, but for the next generation. So they won't suffer the pain and indifference in schools, society and in the workplace. *Be different, be a dyslexic terrorist!*

DYSLEXICS ON REBELLION

GARCÍA MÁRQUEZ AND ME
by Louise Tondeur

"This is Derby everyone," someone called. I
clambered into the van and pulled the dog in after
me. We sat like prisoners lined up inside. One of
them was called Obadiah. He had dreadlocks. He
said to call him Obi like I was pronouncing just the
first two letters. It sounded like Obi-Wan Kenobi
out of Star Wars. He had a girlfriend with woolly
black hair extensions called Noah. I forget the other
names. The dog couldn't sit still. I wrapped my arm
round him.

"Sokay garcon," I whispered but I was nervous
myself. I imagined Obi had a light sabre and a
monk's cape to keep myself calm.

"Have you been on many of these?" I asked. Obi
shrugged.

"We keep it up till they stop, right?" The van
juddered to a halt and Noah opened the door. Obi's
torch confronted me. He grinned.

"You alright?"

"Yeah. Where are we?" I asked.

"You'll see." It was cold. I made out fields and a

few low buildings. The others jumped out behind us. Noah got a screwdriver and worked on the few streetlights so they blinked out. We climbed onto a walkway with only the torch to guide us. It lead us round a car park. García Márquez came with us but Obi made me tie him to the gate once we got clear of the car park. We went hand in hand in a human chain along a path to the back of the farm. The darkness was as thick as stew. Obi was at the front. He pocketed his torch when we got near the farm buildings. A house perched on the side of the hill above the farm. The lights were on but we were hidden behind some low buildings. The ploughing machine looked like a monster, it was so still and silent. It glowed because the moon had just come out from behind a cloud. I smelt hay, manure and sweat. The moon went back behind the clouds and we were cloaked in darkness again. Obi held up a hand.

"OK. Come on." We emerged into an open space. I saw the silhouette of a huge building, like an airport hanger but low on the ground, with a silver roof and a high fence around it. We hid behind a tree with sweeping branches that touched the ground.

"Only one of five," Noah told me in a whisper. We saw someone walk round the building checking the locks. We waited until the figure headed back towards the farm. He made for the same path we had been on a few seconds before. He stopped as if he had heard something. A dog barked in the distance. García Márquez probably. I wished I had left him in the van. The figure moved away. We stayed back while Obi took out his pliers and ran towards the building. He broke a hole in the fence and got a foothold on the outside wall. He moved up a drainpipe and hoisted himself onto the roof. He rooted around in the backpack and unfurled a banner daubed with black paint. It said: *Vivisection must stop now.* He was like Spiderman. He hung from one end of the roof and reached inside the gap at the top of the metal doors with the pliers.

I heard scratching from inside the building as we entered. The smell hit me: urine and dog food. I blinked at the light. The lamps made the air hum. I saw rows of cages and hundreds and hundreds of animals. The smell got stronger. I went over to the nearest one. It was brown with deeper brown eyes. It snarled and ran up and down its cage as outside the rain started. I hadn't ever seen so many animals at once.

"What do we do now?" I said.

"We open the cages," Obi said simply.

"What are they?" I asked.

"Mink," Noah answered.

"Fur, medicine, soap, electrocution, meat what difference does it make?" Obi said. "We're setting them free."

"But won't they die, out there?" I said. I looked out into the field behind us and back at the mink.

"They'll die if we leave them in here," Obi said. "At least we're giving them a chance." He reached into a cage and lifted one of the animals by the scruff of the neck. It was terrified. It looked like a stoat but with a shaggy brown coat. It snarled and tried to bite him so Obi put the animal down. It didn't know what to do at first. It ran over to the wall and stood in the shadows. Then it darted out of the doors into the night. I saw its face light up and the sleet glancing off its fur before it ran out into the darkness.

"What are you waiting for? D'you want to get caught? We could get five years for this." Obi ran to the side of the building and began undoing the cages. The others followed him, opening cages as fast as he did. The growing swarm of mink climbed over each other, snapping and bleeding.

"Come on," Obi said. "Prove yourself." I joined in. The mink continued to swarm. Suddenly the animals began to dart forward out into the night. Someone laughed. I laughed too. Obi held up his hand. He'd heard something. A shot in the darkness. The whine of a dog and police sirens.

"Time to go," he said. We scrabbled across the field in the dark and the mud. The sirens got louder. Obi knew another way out of the farm: through a ditch and over a wall and another field and through a narrow gap in a hedge. We crept back out onto the path on our hands and knees. I heard cars crunching across stony ground in the distance. Obi went on ahead. After a couple of minutes, he ran back towards us. His face looked white.

"Derby come with me," was all he said before he turned and sprinted back the way he came. I followed. I sensed the others behind me. I heard shouting from back near the mink shed. When we got to the place where I had left García Márquez I found the dog on the ground, moaning to himself in a high-pitched whine. I felt tears running down my face, but otherwise I went numb. Obi had taken off his coat. I knelt down and wrapped it around him.

"Garçon," I said. Torches bobbed across the field and the shouts got nearer but I had forgotten about being caught. Obi lifted the dog into my arms.

"They shot him," was all I could say. I felt arms around me one on each side. Another shout.

"We're gonna have to run," Obi said. "Now."

"Come on," Obi said urgently. "Gotta start the van." I cradled García Márquez in Obi's coat while Noah tried to make me run faster. Obi jumped into the van and started the engine. I heard police sirens again. I climbed into the back with the others. Obi put his foot down and we headed off into the darkness. The dog's head rested on my lap. The sirens and shouting died away. García Márquez yelped quietly to himself and I put my face next to his ear and whispered to him.

"I'm sorry. I'm sorry garçon. I'm sorry." He looked up at me. His eyes were red. I mean his pupils were actually red. Five minutes passed until we realised we weren't being followed. Obi drove into the rain, taking random turns, waiting for someone to say something.

"We need to find a vet," Noah said at last. I stayed quiet. Voices buzzed around the van like a swarm of wasps.

"We can't stop. We'll get caught."

"He's gonna die."

"They'll be circulating our pictures already."

"He's gonna die."

"Pictures? No one saw us did they? Who saw us?"

"We're all going to prison for this Obi."

"Pictures of known sympathisers."

"He needs a vet."

"We'll get caught."

"I don't care. We have to get to a vet." The rain was banging hard on the car. I saw lightening in the distance.

"It's ok. It's ok," Noah said. "We'll think of something. Just calm down, ok?" The dog moaned again. I could see the blood on the coat. His eyes rolled back into his head. I felt suddenly cold.

"OK," Obi said. "We find a vet. Derby takes him in. He's not known to the police. Yet." I had to force myself to stay still. I wanted to open the door and run.

"Won't they be looking for someone with an injured lurcher?" someone said.

"Don't care. Get to a vet. I'll take him in," I said.

"Listen. Just take him in," Obi said. "Ask them to look after him and get out as soon as you can. Leave him there. They'll look after him."

"They won't just let him die will they?" I said.

"If it's a vets they care about animals, right Derby?" Obi sounded like he was trying to convince herself.

"OK. OK. That sounds like a plan," Noah said. She was already jabbing at her phone.

"Yeah. Hello. I need the address of a vet that does emergencies. Yeah. Thank you. Thank you."

García Márquez was breathing heavily and his eyes were closed. Still numb, I took the coat in my arms and went across the gravel car park to the animal hospital while Obi hid the van under a tree. A nurse answered the door. She didn't look at me, just at the bundle I was carrying. She took him from my arms. The door closed behind me with a bang. I was in a hallway leading to a waiting room with pictures of flea treatments that smelt of dog biscuits and fur. I had a patch of blood on my jeans from carrying García Márquez. The receptionist helped the nurse with the injured dog. They took him into a room. When she came out she looked at me sharply.

"I need a name," she said.

"He's called García Márquez, ok?" I said.

"No. I need *your* name." She looked like she had suddenly remembered something. She reached for the phone, but the nurse came out.

"I'll deal with this," she said. "Go and wash up." The receptionist had blood on her dress.

"Stay there," she said. She disappeared.

"How did that happened to him?" the nurse asked.

"Dunno. Is he gonna be ok?"

"Too early to tell," she said. The vet called her. As she went into the room, she jerked her head towards the door, telling me to leave. The receptionist was back. She came round the counter. I backed away. A moment later, I was sprinting across the gravel towards the car.

"Drive," I shouted. Obi started the engine as I jumped in.

"They know about it," I said. "Saw it in their faces."

"Is he ok?" Obi said.

"Not sure," I said. "They took him into a room and then"

"It's gonna be fine." Obi drove us down winding

side streets to avoid the main roads. We got lost twice and drove for an hour; we were going round in circles. Finally we found the right road. Obi started wide-eyed out into the night. When I woke up Noah was shaking me. The radio was on.

"We turned it on to hear the news," she said.

"A break in at a mink farm has resulted in the local area being over run with mink. A spokesperson from an animal welfare group said that the mink are not used to the UK environment and will probably die of exposure. These animals should not be approached. Please keep doors and windows closed as they may attack your pets. A receptionist at an animal hospital has identified a suspected member of the gang who freed the mink. He was seeking medical attention for a dog injured during the botched protest at the warehouse, but escaped before she could call the police. The dog has since died." It felt like forever passed before anyone said anything.

"Botched protest. Shit," Obi murmured to himself. The van sunk into muddy silence. The air in the van got heavy. I rested my head against the window. García Márquez was dead.

PAY-BACK
by Jacs Vittles

I could hold one end or the other, but which one
would work best? Rigor had already set in so he
was stiff as a board, which made him easier to move
but I still had to work it out. The last time I saw
him he was sitting in a pub. I went to the bathroom,
came back and, bam, he was gone. The stool he'd
been sitting on was overturned, the old guy in
the corner was nursing his beer and all the chat
had stopped. Feet shuffled but no-one looked up.
Unasked questions hung in the air.

I grabbed the shoulders of his jacket and dragged
him towards the stairs. Filthy concrete tugging
at the heels of his shoes until they came off, one
after the other. One grim light was flicking on the
landing below but I could see enough. His feet
dropped heavily against each step as I shuffled
backwards, carefully feeling for each stair-edge
before gingerly moving back some more. I lost my
grip of one shoulder and he tilted precariously
towards the gaping space where the banister should
have been. I let go of the other side and stood up to

catch my breath, his head held tight between my feet, shoulders jammed against my shins.

We'd been close, once. We understood each other as we were making our mark, back then, on the streets. I was a bit older than him but he'd had all the charm. We always went for the same girls but he was the one that got them first. When he'd got tired of them they'd come to me, just so as they could still hang around with him. Bastard. He'd be there, with his big shoulders, even bigger grin and tight pants. The Mullet King, we called him. He loved that.

I could hear voices a few floors above and froze. A door opened and something heavy clattered onto the concrete.

"Get off my back, will you! I'll do it tomorrow!" then the door slammed shut again. Breath leaking from my lungs, I looked down and saw his dull, empty eyes looking back at up at me. Bastard. Not much of a mullet now, eh?

He'd always had the fun, running around in his fast cars, people hanging on his every word, waiting for his pearls of wisdom. Being taken into his confidence, one by one. Being made to feel special, then setting each of them against each other. Trying to score points off each other to win the favour of the father-figure. The cultivated air of mystery that surrounded him like a force field. He fed off their servility. He nurtured their vulnerability. They revered him like a god. Then, one by one, he'd crush them. Demolish their self-respect. Make them feel like scum in his presence. Cast them out from his inner sanctum and stoke their longing to be redeemed, reinstated. He'd wait until that perfectly timed moment of abject misery; then he'd forgive them. Now he owned their very souls – and they were grateful. It was his validation.

I saw it, over and over again. I marvelled at his ability to keep doing it. To keep sucking people into his web, gorging on their obedience then spitting out the bones until contrition rekindled their own reason for being. How did he do it? How could he get away with it? But maybe he hadn't.

Grabbing at his shoulders, I resumed the slow retreat down the stairs. Dragging him backwards through the detritus he'd had a hand in propagating. How fitting that this should be where his own life had been snuffed out. One clean shot from a skilled marksman. The flicking light now several storeys above, I pushed at the broken door with my backside and dragged my quarry to a resting place beside the garbage recess. I pulled out a pack of cigarettes, flicked the lighter and drew heavily to fill my lungs. A dog barked behind a closed door.

George Michael had been his hero, until he'd realised he was gay. He'd had the blonde streaks, pulled up his shirt collars and pushed up his jacket sleeves to show his bronzed, muscular arms. No track marks in those days. He'd loved the Bananarama chicks and oozed his charm to Alison Moyet soundtracks. Then, *"The Only Way is Up!"* he'd spit through gritted teeth, as he was screwing them hard against the wall, the floor, the table, anywhere that had no vestige of dignity and no comfort for his prey. They adored him but to him they were meat, to be consumed, chewed up and spat out like discarded lumps of gristle. The only one this guy had loved, was himself.

Lorraine had tried. God-love-her, how she'd tried. I know because it was me that'd picked up the pieces, every time. She'd try to give him what he wanted; obedience, subservience. She was a doormat to wipe his dirt on. When young Kieran came along I'd promised to stand by her, to look after her, but I knew he wasn't mine. We both knew, but neither of us said. If hope was a currency, she'd have been rich; and now Kieran has the mantle. He doesn't carry it so well but he might get through the nightmare that is young adulthood in this God-forsaken place.

His stiff corpse was resting at my feet. I pushed at it, lifting one side and turning it over, ramming his face down into the dirt. I'd wanted to do that when he was alive. It gave me no comfort now. In the darkness I could just make out the entry point. No exit wound on the other side. The shot had been fired from distance. The bullet still lodged in his brain. But surprisingly little blood.

I'd seen more blood in Bosnia. It was supposed to be my escape but had turned out to be just another living hell. She'd asked me not to go, not to sign up. She'd said she couldn't live without me. But the minute my back was turned I knew he'd come sniffing around again and she'd open her legs to him, like a bitch on heat. And she did. The rumours had soon got back to me. How he was screwing her. How Kieran was roaming the streets at night, being taken in by neighbours. How he'd turn up at school with bruises and how Lorraine kept 'walking into cupboard doors'.

I didn't go back when I got out. I didn't even tell them I was back. I didn't want to return to the old crowd, the old ways. It was complicated. I had some thinking to do. I'd moved on. I found some digs and got a job as a bouncer at a posh club up West.

Then I saw him, one time. He didn't see me but it was him, alright. Getting out of his Beemer with a gaggle of tarts all around him. Skirts up their arses, heels too high to walk on. Invisible clouds of cheap perfume. Mr Flash, covered in bling. Sometimes I'd be swapped with the lads inside and I'd see him there, doing his business with guys wearing shades or sometimes just with the girls. Always with his white powder. You could see it in his eyes, bright and shiny like a ferret. He never saw me. I never made contact.

One day, I was going off my shift and the boss pulled me aside. He said he'd heard I'd been a squaddie and that I was handy with a gun. He said he could use a good man like me and that it would be worth my while, if I did a clean job. The door job didn't pay much and I was short of cash, so I listened.

He had all the gear, night vision, telescopic lenses, the lot. The first one was hard. I couldn't shake off the memory of the village, the blood, the torn limbs, the carnage. But it got easier.

I reversed the car up to the garbage recess. He wasn't tall so I was able to load him in the back, wedged at an angle, his head resting against the side window, as if he was asleep. The disused quarry was East off the M25. It would take me about an hour. I shoved in a CD. Sting. *Every Breath You Take*. Apt. Three a.m. is the best time to hit this road. It's the only time it's not a car park. I cranked up the air con to neutralise the smell.

The boss was the nearest thing to honourable that you'd get in this shit world. I knew that if I did a good job, he'd see me right. He called me his *Numero Uno* now, but I'd earned it. I knew there were raw ends and if I pulled too hard the whole thing would unravel. So I didn't pull. I obeyed orders. I didn't ask questions. Just like I'd been trained to do. The only difference now was that I had a bank balance worth looking at.

It was when I was walking home one night that I saw him. Slumped in a doorway on a pile of filthy newspaper. I squatted down next to him, cupped his soft, downy chin in my hand and lifted his face towards me. Kieran. The eyes were empty. He was breathing but there was no life. I called an ambulance and walked away.

He did this. His hand hadn't been on the needle, or the wrap, but he did it. Whichever way you looked at it, *he* was responsible.

She'd managed to get herself to the station to meet me but that was the sum total of her effort. And the first thing she did was tap me for her next fix. I'd never touched the stuff. Most of the lads had been into it to relieve the boredom, and to escape the truth of what following orders meant they had to do. But I liked to be in control and that stuff took you up or down. Either way, you weren't in control. I'd seen what it did to people. What it did to my mates. What it did to Kieran. And now, what it had done to Lorraine.

She was a shadow of the woman she'd once been. The woman I'd known and had tried to help. She was still talking about him. Asking if I'd seen him. Eyes pinned. Soul long since left her body. She never once mentioned Kieran.

This was my fifth contract. The first one gave me the shits, but like I said, it got easier. And it was made easier because I knew I was removing another piece of scum off the streets. I knew the boss trusted me because my last one had been higher up the food chain and had gone really well. It had made the papers that he'd gone missing but the cops didn't have a clue. I'm too good. But this one felt different.

I had to suss him out first. Asked around. Got to know his patterns. Got to know his contacts. Took a while, but it was worth it. But I got a bit careless and the word got out that someone was looking for him. He didn't know who; then I saw him in the pub. Didn't think he'd clocked me until I got back from taking a leak – and he'd gone. See, it had started to get personal for me and that's dangerous. You let your guard down. Big mistake.

I'd gone after him when he left the pub and followed him into the estate. Stupid fool. He was running home. So out of his tree it never occurred to him that'd be the first place I'd look, so the last place to go. I'd already been up there and worked out the best angle. I stopped, caught my breath, turned on my heels and made my way towards a high-rise on the edge of the estate. I took my time. I wanted him to think he was safe. It was still daylight so the timing wasn't right.

In position, I had the perfect angle, looking down. I could see him through the open window, sitting at the edge of the filthy mattress, on the floor up against the wall. The bed frame long since gone. I looked through the sights. He was getting his gear ready. No big shoulders and tight pants now. No hangers-on. No bling. No nothing. Just him, and his habit.

I saw him shoot up, head bowed in concentration. Then slowly and gradually, he rolled backwards to lie flat. His head turned away from me towards the wall. Perfect.

They say that good dealers don't touch the stuff themselves. It's too risky. They leave that to the pushers. And that had been his downfall. The means by which people had come to see him for what he was – a miserable, snivelling junkie. His empire had crumbled and his obsequious shadows had faded away, one by one. They'd reclaimed their souls – then given them away again, to someone else.

I had plenty of time. I needed the dusk and he wasn't going anywhere, any time soon. I lit a cigarette, drew in deep and sat back to watch the smoke making shapes in the still air.

I nipped the lit end between my thumb and forefinger, checked my watch, opened the case and started to assemble the equipment. I looked through the sights again. He hadn't moved. I lined up, breathed deeply and squeezed. There was an imperceptible shudder in his body as his head nudged sideways into the wall. Silence.

It was too early to move him. Still too much light, but I needed to go back later to tidy up the loose ends. The boss hated loose ends, that's why he trusted me. He knew I didn't leave any. I went back to the lock-up and left the gear then went to get something to eat. I had to do the job on an empty stomach, but not the clear-up.

I never asked the boss about the contracts but I knew that this one had been personal. He'd owed him money, grassed him up, and, he'd hit on his woman. The boss had done time for possession and had been stewing on it. Now, it was pay-back.

I turned off the road, killed the lights and pulled up at the side entrance. I got out and pushed at the gate. He'd told me it would be left unlocked, and it gave way easily. No sign of life. I moved the car slowly into the yard, along a dirt track behind some buildings. Just enough light from the moon. I followed the track into the base of the pit, pulled up and cut the engine.

I looked over into the back and saw his face bathed in eerie light. A face so familiar to me, and yet so distant. There was a serenity about his expression that suggested he'd been dead before the shot lodged in his brain. It would account for the lack of blood. His fix too pure.

I got out leaving the driver's door open, went round to the back and took out the can. I twisted off the lid and breathed in the heady, toxic fumes, opened the rear door and doused him in petrol. Soaked the front seats, popped the bonnet and emptied the rest over the still warm engine, just for good measure.

I needed a delay so I lit a couple of rags and left them burning in the wheel arches. I took a couple of paces backwards then turned and walked up the track, tracing the route I'd driven down. The bike was there as planned, behind some outhouses and as I turned the key in the ignition, a muffled – *boom!* A plume of smoke rose into the distant air. No-one but me to witness it. Two more rumbled explosions.

A moment's pause before starting the engine and

slipping the bike into gear. Moving forward as my feet lifted from the ground, I thought of the warning my old dad had given me, all those years ago. We get what we deserve in this life. He could never have known it would be the portent of fratricide. Goodbye brother.

THE MAVERICK
by Dee Kirkby

"There he is!" Cody spotted the tatty cat climbing
over the fence in the garden and rushed out to
make a fuss of him with his sisters following close
behind, slamming the door in their excitement.

"I think it's really mean of you to name him after
some old boxer."

"Mean? That's all you know. Joey DeJohn was a
legend! Even if he did have a scrunched up face."

Sandi and Lizzy secretly thought him too sweet
to be named after a sportsman and agreed with
each other that 'Marmalade' suited him better.
They didn't want to complain though, for they
knew that if they didn't go along with Cody's
choice he would be grumpy and impatient with
them until they agreed with his choice of name.
The girls knew how to keep the peace; they'd
watched their mother defer to their father for
years now. Each day the children snuck food
from their meagre portions to feed to Joey. Cody
and his sisters would crowd happily round Joey,
marvelling that he managed to purr as he ate.

During meals he would allow them to smooth his fur, arching his back against their passing hands. Their back yard was little more than concrete and coarse grass but these discomforts blurred during these stolen moments in time, gifting them with the illusion that their world was a calm and peaceful place. A reality filled with the soothing sensations that were a by product of stroking a warm, purring, *although distinctly smelly*, giver of comfort.

While Cody's mother (occasionally encouraged these stolen moments with Joey, the children knew their father most certainly would not. No childhood magic for Edward's brood *thankyouverymuch*! He believed that the sooner they faced the harsh realities of life, the better prepared they would be. That very day he caught them enjoying their unacceptable moments of cat magic when he came home early from work, there had been a fire at the factory and it was now closed until the damage could be repaired. The 'fwhick' of the gate latch disengaging from the catch penetrated their happy haze too slowly for them to be able to shoo Joey away. They looked at each other in horror knowing that only their father used the back gate. Why had he come home early? They knew that the very act of feeding Joey, when their father wasn't supposed to be home, would convince him that they were being deliberately deceitful. Guilt blushed across their faces. As one they turned and, too scared to look at his face, they instead watched his boots make contact with the concrete, each loud step bringing him closer to Joey.

Despite their pathetic attempts to shield him, Edward could see the mangy cat licking the pavement. No work equalled no money and the sight of them feeding a stray incensed him beyond reason. He reached between the girls easily parting their joined hands. He took a half step then followed through with his other leg. The toe of his boot connected with Joey's body transferring enough momentum to send him flying over the fence. The children heard Joey squeal once. Then painfully weighted silence descended on both sides of the fence. As one, they turned toward their father, hollow with the knowledge that they would be next to feel the impact of his wrath.

He glared at them and then words poured from his mouth, riding the crest of his anger.

"You don't have a clue do 'ya? Not a clue."

They flinched, nodded and then hastily shook their

heads confused.

Edward's face darkened

"Food costs money, something which you contribute none of. I don't work my ass off so that you can feed perfectly good food to mangy strays!"

Snatching up the remains of the fish, he kicked aside a sun bleached plastic ball and stomped into the house. The children were too scared by what Joey's continued silence might mean to give much thought to the fact that they remained unpunished.

"Feeding strays won't make amends for your past. For God's sake woman, what's done is done. Stop looking back before I...."

Guiltily relieved at their escape, the children tuned out their father's voice and loitered outside whispering Joey's name, hoping for a meow in response, until their mother called them for supper. Cody and his sisters slunk in. After quickly washing their hands they sat on the wooden bench between the chilly outside facing wall and table. Their father was po-faced at the head of the table, making eye contact only with the television which sat precariously on a narrow shelf above their mother's chair. Betty served them their meal, lips pressed into a thin line, her face as pale and bleak as the soup she put before them. Cody and his sisters looked down at their bowls and realised with horror that this was their punishment; the fish scales floated iridescently on top of the thin milky broth. Edward slurped his soup loudly. The rest of the family quietly tried to swallow without the food touching their tongue. Cody kept his gaze on the table for fear his rage would be visible in his eyes. The view of scarred and pitted beige surface did little to calm him. He wondered why the heat of his angry stare didn't burn holes in the table. Cody flinched when the phone rang in the next room and again when his father heaved himself out of the chair to go answer it.

Cody grabbed the tin of sewing machine oil that sat on the window ledge behind him and squirted, then stirred some into his father's soup bowl. The thin walls were no barrier to the peaks and troughs of the angry sounding mutters that emanated from their father's side of the phone conversation in the next room. Oddly, the silence that followed the phone making contact with its cradle was no less disturbing than the noise that had preceded it. When their father returned to the table, they were all innocently stirring their soup. He sat down casting a suspicious glare over them before spooning the remainder of his soup into his mouth with his eyes fixed unwaveringly on the television for the rest of the meal.

Cody dared not look at his sisters when their father picked up his spoon. He could feel them trembling on either side of him as they fought to suppress the urge to giggle hysterically. The sharp edge of their mother's palpable fear quickly rendered them poker faced as their father spooned the way through his bowlful, rarely dropping his glance from the telly.

◎

The repeated sound of his father's footfall on the landing between the toilet and bedroom that night gave Cody a funny feeling in his stomach, the kind he got when he was a little bit scared and a little bit happy. To stop himself from feeling bad for feeling happy, he pulled his dictionary out from under his blanket. Turning to the correct page in the M section he once again read the reassuring definition for maverick: *Someone who exhibits great independence in thought and action*

Cody the Maverick made sure the book couldn't

be seen in its hiding place under his bed before he fell asleep.

ANIMUS
by Kristen McHenry

For the Egyptian cobra who escaped from the Bronx Zoo,
late March 2011

I admit I was pulling
for the cobra.
A part of us
always roots for the escapee
be they venomous, rabid or
otherwise sinister. We like the idea of something
unpredictable on the loose,
although the zookeepers assured us that
cobras don't like open spaces; they're
more afraid us, blah blah blah. To my
disappointment, they did find her
finally, curled up small and dry somewhere.

It's just that I wanted to see her
rise up, terrorize the Bronx
with her black hood and oozing fangs, chase
hot dog vendors down the street and hiss,
I'm here, bitches.

Not that she didn't scare me a little, too—that restless,
loose and hungry thing.

GLITTERING EYE
by Anneliese Evans

Set some time after *The Rime of the Ancient Mariner*
by Samuel Taylor Coleridge

Part I The Deal

"Of waters blue and waters green,
Of depths unknown and core unseen
Employ the mysteries of the deep,
What lies below is yours to reap
But what is there to have, to glean,
Of murky climes and souls unclean"?

"Go forth and seek," so beckoned he
"To venture down beneath the sea
Beyond the wreck, beyond the freight
Where hapless sailors met their fate.
The deepest depths are my decree,
Go forth and toil to set it free."

And so they lined the musty keel,
These lowly folk, who sought a deal

Poor and reckless, feckless kind,
Whose poverty enthused to find
Whatever they could loot or steal,
A daring scheme to fleece a meal.

So Captain eyed this fruitless pack
And eager, poised, they eyed him back
"So men…" in rapturous tones cried he
"So men of fortune you all shall be,
To plot, to scheme, to plan attack
Into the gloom, into the black."

And so incensed with oafish glee
The mob of nine did thus agree
And with their pittance worth of wares,
Abandoned heart, discarded cares.
Yet Earth would sooner set them free,
To sell their souls onto the sea.

Part II Setting off

"The Morning Star shall grant consent-
We'll leave at dawn at his intent".
Said Captain to his rowdy men-
Whose totalled crew comprised of ten.
Indeed, the kindly star had sent

A good, west wind and off they went!

From south along the wayward shore
The wind held high and sunlight bore
On cliffs that arched across the cove,
Dividing as the helmsman drove,
This vessel that had ne'er before
Entered through this ocean door.

Now east along the cliffs of white,
Until the land was out of sight,
Sun's rays dappled on the swell
As dancing waves served to propel-
She dazzled in the morning light,
Seaward bound, now all was bright.

Good grace; the crew in winsome mode,
Embraced their watery new abode,
They drained the keg and drank the rum,
They flew the flag and beat the drum.
What merriment, it surely showed,
That nothing ill they could forebode.

As calm, still waters swirled around
The night crept in without a sound

Now weary from their merry feast,
The deck was still, the music ceased
And softly did the waves resound,
Whilst surging from their watery ground.

Part III Standing Still

The ship rose up, t'was day anew.
Her haughty bow cut proudly through
The dormant sea, whose depths were stirred,
Alas a wrath was duly spurred,
A force that slowly, slowly grew
Amid that great expanse of blue.

And as that wrath began to grow
The haughty ship began to slow
So fraught were they and restless too,
Moved only by the wind that blew
But when that wind refused to blow
Her square-rigged sails slacked down low.

Alas the sea, her mighty will,
More deadly yet, when she was still.
And seaman groaned, their throats were dry,
The fiery sun beat from the sky,
Nor Captain with his ocean skill

Could move his ship amid the spill.

Part IV The Curse

Aboard that deck so parched and sear,
There was a hoary buccaneer.
Between the sun with its' fiery rays,
And ancient eyes, that burnt and blazed,
A shadow gliding by, mast high,
Was captured in a glittering eye.

Through the lens of his flashing eye,
He fixed his gaze onto the sky
Betwixt the deck, the mast and skies
The mariner dropped down mesmerized.

And as he dropped, dry boards did creak
The crew looked on, would they dare speak?
Yet faster than his senses fled,
Were they returned on wings of dread.

"Avast," cried he, "beware, beware
I bring aboard my cross to bear."
His yellow eyes did burn and flare
"The cursed black spot is there, is there"
He thrust his hand out in the air

They gasped, aghast-despair, despair!

"Have mercy men" His hollow plea,
"I am an old man of the sea
And now the time my soul to sell
My sins too terrible to tell"
In wrathful fright, that failed to see,
They cast their thoughts to mutiny.

Though impotent their wrath to prove,
Their bitterness they could not soothe.
In this great void, it had been shown
They were alone, so all alone,
For life nor death could mere mortals move,
Or cursed black spots could mortal men remove.

So days to nights still all adrift,
The wretched curse refused to lift,
A glassy haze stretched overhead
And sank below the dank sea bed
Bright strikes of sky light marked the shift,
Black clouds rushed in and it was swift.
The rain came pouring from the skies
The stagnant sea began to rise,
And joy behold, it was such bliss

To quench dry souls with Heaven's kiss
But joy rolled in in cruel disguise
And burnt and flared through yellow eyes.

Part V The Great Descent

And there he stood upon the mast
With eyes that flickered in the blast
With flailing arms held high he raged
Now like a prisoner uncaged.

Unleashed, unbound, the mariner wailed
"Through lands I've traipsed, on seas I've sailed
But still it stalks me - ghostly foe!
That creature shot by my cross-bow".

"And my decrepit life won't cease
Let Death-In-Life be my release
I shall retell my tale no more,
Take me downwards to Earth's core!"

So began a great commotion,
That bubbled like a witch's potion,
And swirled and whirled and opened wide
In fast and round and circular motion
And sucked them down as they all cried

"Whose hand unplugs the ocean?"

For she went down and round and round
It coaxed her nearer, pound by pound
And whipped her hull and slapped her deck
Down and down and side to side

It spurned and turned and opened wide
And beat her downwards with the tide
And stripped her bare and beat her deck
The haughty ship dropped down a wreck.

Part VI Towards Earth's Core

And they clung on in desperate plea,
Against the wrath of that cruel sea.
Poor mortal men, against the might
Now dark, so dark, devoid of light,
What chances now have they to flee
From this tempestuous entity?
Then came a summon from the sky,
The ship dropped downward from up high,
And all at once the motion ceased
For calm had come to quell the beast,
But met with unbelieving sighs
It pierced the dark with flashing eyes.

Now darkness shrouded one and all
And echoes bounded off a wall-
For deep, deep down in this abyss
The wretched curse would still persist,
For round the corner, what was more,
Blazed the fires of Earth's core!

Through mystic caverns dark and wide,
Deep, darkened seas did not subside.
And Captain with his rowdy men
Were ghostly silent, for that was then,
Now pale and lost, in spectral stride,
A skeletal ship did softly glide.

And onwards, downwards with Earth's tilt,
Towards the dagger, blade and hilt,
Where fires leap and lava flies,
And flames burn red in demon's eyes-
That mariner drives devoid of guilt
To that damned place the Devil built.

For here the waters stir below
And boil and bubble and quickly slow,
And through the dark, the floor glints red
As seas transform to molten lead,

And shadows jump and come and go
And reflect the light with crimson glow.

Part VII At Earth's Core

And so they came to Earth's dark core
Had they expected something more?
Would treasure troves and coins of gold
Be their great bounty to behold?
So joyful, they'd return to shore,
No longer feckless, weak and poor?

But so it was by weak decree,
They'd led themselves so greedily,
Entrapped inside the bowels of earth
This fruitless kind observed their worth
And spoke the truth explicitly
"We are the scum of land and sea"
But he, who had much more to fear,
That haggard, hoary buccaneer
Though scripted by another pen,
His sins cannot be told again.
And fate emerged - so it was clear,
His final breath was drawing near.

The end came quick, as he was flung-

One fiery swoop and he was slung,
From out the ship, his being plucked
And by the flames, his life-blood sucked.
For those who saw it, how it stung
It burned the eyes and scorched the tongue.

But now the ghastly fray recedes,
For Hell has taken what it needs
And as the curse begins to lift,
Once more Earth's core begins to shift,
The molten flow beneath them leads,
That broken ship, it now proceeds.

Part VIII The Great Ascent

And so began the great ascent
Up and up and up they went,
The surface neared, how it seethed,
With melted rocks, the rubble heaved.
Towards the sky and through the vent
Were fiery, fountain torrents sent.

For as the pressure grew and grew
Purged from the deep, hot fragments flew
And with the thrust, it cut its course,
A magma river there did force

And from the crater, it did spew,
A blighted ship and battered crew.

Running down the mountain side
Meandering with mazy stride,
It met with cooling streams and blended,
Here the lava trail ended.
The pure springs did now provide
Lush greenery spread far and wide.

The ship, it went at rapid pace,
Careering down that mountain face
And all at once the skylarks sang.
Then further down a church bell rang.
Now, could it be, this route they trace,
Returns them to a well known place?

Part IX The Return

To the horizon eyes were glued,
It was a splendid thing they viewed.
And in the distance, all shone bright
That sheltered cove, those cliffs of white.
No longer were this crew subdued
Their tortured spirits now renewed.

From passing through the harbour door
Against cruel tides they reached the shore,
Yet through the terror, pain and woe,
Did they have anything to show?
Where were the coins, the gold, the store?
Weren't they as hapless as before?

With not a penny to their name,
It is a thought who they might blame
Yet strange to see, that when on land,
Each shook their Captain by the hand-
For these eight men, they weren't the same,
They'd sold their souls in search of fame.

Although no riches did they find,
They'd heed a lesson for mankind.
For as they made it up the hill,
The distant bells were ringing still.
With moral conscience redefined,
They left the harbour side behind.

Part X The Glittering Eye

But they'd not known they'd had a spy
Who first had seen them from the sky
And on the mast, his chosen perch,

He watched them entering the church

And when at last he took to flight,
His yellow eyes flashed in the light,
For as he stretched his wings to fly,
He bid them well with glittering eye.

GREEN PARK
by Matthew Scurfield

He screeches to a halt with empty rage
Consumes a broken bench
Stopped in his tracks
Out of control
Whilst daffodils peak
A frustrated story at the end of a page
Mid flow
Nowhere to go
Screams
From days into night
The trees they speak
Always there
Raging
Wash away wounds in the pouring rain
A mottled dewdrop glints
Green Park's alright
Natures wink
Constantly changing
Dependable
Something right that seems undone
Whilse the clouds reveal the warmth of the sun.

THE DYSLEXIC IMAGINATION

DARWIN'S CHILDREN
by Elizabeth Tasker

The single most devastating event for the human race occurred when my father got a new job.

We were thrilled. Well, more accurately, I was thrilled, but since I was currently not speaking to either Edith or Tilly, that amounted to the same thing. I hoisted myself up onto a tall stool as Dad organised his new work space. Sterilised pots on the shelf to the left, glass chemical vials against the wall, paper on the far right away from any spills. It was a spotless expanse of brilliant white. I put my hand down on the countertop and felt the tell-tale pull of skin as whatever I had forgotten was on my palm transferred itself to the serialised surface. Tentatively, I tapped my fingers, trying to look nonchalant.

Dad raised his eyebrows. "So, Addy, first day at your new school tomorrow?" He walked to one of the sinks and picked up a cloth, returning to hold it over the spot where my hand was stuck to the counter.

Guiltily, I peeled the offending appendage away,

leaving undeniable evidence of my visit in pink jam.

"Yes," I said noncommittally, debating whether I could wipe my sticky palm on the underside of the work surface.

Dad caught my hand before the thought had morphed into an action and wiped it clean with the cloth. I looked up to see the smile tugging at the corners of his mouth. He flicked water onto my nose, startling a laugh out of me.

"This school will be better." His tone was serious as he met my eyes. "This city isn't like our old home. They employed me as a research scientist after all." His eyes rose from my face to flick around the laboratory, its lights bright against the darkness of the night outside.

"It's still not a breeder lab, Dad," I pointed out and then immediately regretted it as I saw his face fall.

"No," he agreed as he forced the smile back onto his face. "but just because the genetic patterns stored here won't ever be in a new baby does not mean we can't learn from them. It's no less important. Non-breeders are no less important."

My eyes dropped and began to pick out the

pattern of tiles on the vinyl floor as I resisted the urge to touch my neck. This process was disturbed by long fingers that poked into my field of view and then blurred out of focus as my nose was tweaked. I looked up, feeling half-amused and half-exasperated.

"Right?" Dad's eyes were smiling down at me. It was impossible not to smile back.

"Right."

◎

There were three people at my birth. My mother, a necessity since I was inside her, my father and my biological father. The hospital was used to such arrangements and had provided two chairs, but only my father sat. He held my mother's hand and squeezed it, his expression both anxious and excited. His brother, the sperm donor, leaned against the door, eying the backside of the nurses as they walked past.

When, squealing and bright red, I came into the world, my father wiped away tears from his eyes as he let me grasp one of his fingers. My biological father looked down at my scrunched up face, grinned and clapped his brother on the shoulder.

"I've given you guys a good one!" His expression made it clear that he was delighted he would not be the one bringing me up. He flicked at the black ink mark behind my father's left ear. "Heading out to Shanghai tonight. Let me know if you guys want a number three!"

He was gone. I did not meet him again until he came for dinner eight years later when Tilly was conceived.

◎

I looked down at my tablet computer and scowled. The red triangle flashed on the screen beside the question I had left uncompleted. I raised my head to glare around at the hall of new students bent over their own registration forms. Two thirds of the desks surrounding me were empty, their occupants having already left for their first class. My vexed expression was caught by the invigilating teacher who walked briskly down the room to my side.

"Is there a problem, uh..." She glanced down at the top of my tablet's screen. "Addison?"

I took a deep breath. "I don't see why this question is necessary." I lifted the slender rectangle for her to see.

The teacher took the tablet from my hand and squinted at the type face.

"Breeder?" She frowned. "Well, Addison, we have to know."

"Why?"

My question, or perhaps the bare-faced nature of it, caught her by surprise.

"It's a basic fact about you. Like ... gender."

Now that she mentioned it, I did not see why my sex was relevant to my education either. However, having endured a week of torment upon my return from hospital with Edith referring to me as an 'it' until Mum caught her, I was not about to contest anything that might lead to me not being referred to as a female.

"Does it affect what education I get?" I met the teacher's eyes squarely. "Or are you asking if I need to be excused from classes where giving birth during the mid-terms is a prerequisite?"

"Do not be ridiculous!" The teacher's glasses slipped down her nose and she caught the bridge with one finger. "Unless you have had an illness that has addled your brains, then you are the same as everyone else."

"Then why?"

"Just fill it in, Addison. Do you really want to cause a scene on your first day at school?" Her eyes raked the pale skin of my neck.

I folded my arms, my jaw set.

"Oh for heaven's sake!" In exasperation, the teacher tapped my tablet with her stylus twice and then passed it back to me. I looked down at the illuminated surface.

Registered student: #3479441
Addison Lambeth.
Female.
Age 15.
Breeder.
Class 20b.

I swallowed and lifted a hand to run fingers over the shadowed flesh just below my left ear. I had just been told it was unimportant. So be it. I scooped up my bag and left the hall. Time to find class 20b.

◉

I cried when they tattooed me. The area was numb and I was too young to fully understand the implications of what this meant, but the unhappy look in my father's face caused me to bawl my 10 year old eyes out.

When I was returned to my parents in the hospital waiting room, Mum hugged me while Dad pressed a wet cotton ball to the abused region of my neck. I cried harder as it stung my skin.

"Darling," my mother reproved. "I'm sure they've cleaned it."

Dad did not meet her eyes. "This will help," he mumbled. "It's from the lab." When he pulled the swab away, it was dark with ink.

◎

There were a whole series of doors leading to Dad's lab, but none of them were locked. I banged my way through, sucking on a coconut bubble tea that I probably should have disposed of before entering the building, but nobody said anything.

When I reached Dad's bench it was just after 5pm and the room appeared deserted. Unstoppered bottles, discarded test-tubes and unmatched latex gloves sprawled over the other neighbouring countertops. It had a decided Mary Celeste feel to it as if the scientists had suddenly vanished, mid work-flow. I entertained myself imagining an alien abduction in which the entire lab had been teleported into space.

Suddenly concerned about that possibility, I levered myself onto a stool and balanced precariously until I spied my father. He was at the far end of the lab in a glass walled enclosure that contained racks of frozen materials. I noisily sucked up the last of my drink and jumped off the stool with a clatter.

The double door to the chamber was shut to keep the temperature down, but I pressed my face up against the clear wall. My nose flattened and I puffed out my cheeks in a blow fish pose ready for Dad to turn around. As I stood poised, my eyes drifted along the shelves of test-tubes in their refrigeration units. All had a panel listing their contents. Taking care to keep my amusing face in position, I strained my eyes to read the one closest to me.

NAME: *Anderson, Miranda*   PFD: *Malaria*
NAME: *Apple, Sylvester*   PFD: *Meningitis*
NAME: *Araman, Kevin*   PFD: *Leukaemia*
NAME: *Aspen, Rebecca*   PFD: *Septicaemia*
NAME: *Atwood, Patrick*   PFD: *Mumps*

My cheeks deflated with a sound like a plunger and resumed a scowl as Dad spotted me and came out through the door.

"Since when have we sterilised someone after they've been cured of mumps?" I demanded. "It's not a Potentially Fatal Disease!"

About to bend over to kiss me, Dad paused and also looked through the glass wall at the nearest set of samples.

"It depends how badly he had it," he explained. "If he would have died or even become sterile without intervention, then his genes cannot be passed onto the next generation." He peeled off his gloves and then lifted my empty drink cup from my hands, dropping both into a trash can.

I stared into the depths of the sample racks. "Did my egg sample arrive?" I made my inquiry sound casual, as if I cared nothing about the only living part of my ovaries being in a test tube, not my body.

An arm wrapped around my shoulders as Dad kissed me on the head.

"Last week," he said. "Same as mine. We're side by side."

I managed a smile. It was a nice thought.

"Although heaven knows when all this will be

documented correctly on the system." Dad let go of me and gazed around the messy work surfaces. "I'd recommend not falling sick for at least another six months." He sighed and began to gather empty beakers for washing. "Currently, the entire record of your life probably consists of your school questionnaire."

I grinned. "I came top in science." I walked to a sink and turned the tap on for Dad to rinse the glassware. "I might be selected to represent the school in the national science fair next month."

Dad's smile was so wide he looked as though his face would split in two.

"Your talents are finally being recognised. I knew this school would be different." He waited until my hands were clear before emptying any residue liquids into the drain.

"Hmm." I made a non-committal noise, my eyes sliding to the window. Across from this building was another lab, its people still busy at work. They wore crisp white coats with ID badges hanging from the top pocket as they moved like a well oiled machine between benches of neatly arranged experiments.

"Daddy!" The gurgling voice jerked me guiltily

back around to see a small blond bombshell launch herself across the lab.

"H-hey Tilly!" Making a fast decision, Dad dropped the two lids he was holding onto two uncovered petri dishes, freeing his hands so he could scoop up his youngest daughter. She promptly bit his finger and then looked disgusted.

"Daddy, you taste of swimming pool water!" The small pink tongue hung out in repulsion.

"It's what I use to keep my hands clean," Dad explained. He looked across at me and gestured to the door where Mum was waiting, holding Tilly's small pink coat and the one I had dumped across a chair. "Shall we go?"

◎

"One place for Mum." I stopped at one end of the dining room table. Bending my knees, I dipped low enough for Tilly to press one wet hand against the glass countertop. A square 10 inch section of the table glowed blue as the sterilising UV beam swept underneath it.

Tilly pushed her thumb back into her mouth as the cleaned piece of glass flipped 180 degrees and rose an inch to form a platform for food.

"Don't do that," I told her. "You need that hand another four times yet." I moved one place along as Tilly reluctantly withdrew her thumb and pressed her small palm against the table for a second time. Her other hand wrapped around my neck as I carried her on one hip around the room until five places had been set for dinner.

Edith twirled through the door, her skirts rising gracefully in a waft of magnolia perfume.

"I've met the boy I am going to marry," she announced dramatically. Tilly sneezed.

"Quite," I muttered.

"Is she sick?!" Edith's cornflower blue stare swung accusingly onto Tilly. "I can't stay here if she's sick!"

I rolled my eyes as Tilly buried her face in my shoulder. "Some sister you are," I told Edith angrily.

"I've just met the love of my life." Edith pirouetted on the spot, her eyes lifting to the heavens in an expression of angelic delight. "When we marry, we want a large family. Which means..." Her eyes dropped in time to see me mouthing along to her heartfelt declarations.

Well, it was not like I had not heard them two

hundred times before.

Edith's whimsical look morphed into a scowl. "It means I can't risk becoming sick. Tilly can't surrogate for us both!"

I hugged my little sister tighter. "Like she'd surrogate for you anyway."

My older sister tossed her mane of blond curls, looking as haughty as her 17 years would allow. "All the more reason why I should be out of this house." She shot me a nauseating smile. "If you're nice to me, I'll name one of my daughters Addison."

"Edith." Mum backed in from the kitchen, carrying a crock-pot. There was a note of warning in her voice.

Edith swept up to plant a kiss on her cheek. "I'm going out," she said, adding before there could be objections, "ask Addy how she did in her science exam." She was gone, the door swinging shut behind her.

Mum turned in vexation from the doorway to where I still stood with Tilly.

"Who is it this time?" She placed the pot on the table. "And what is this about your science exam? It's your best subject."

I glared at the spot where my sister had just

exited as I hooked a chair out from under the table with one foot.

"We didn't get a name. I'm sure it will be on the wedding invites though." I put Tilly down in the seat, sliding it up to the table.

"Addy," Mum reproved, walking across to tuck a napkin into Tilly's tee-shirt. Tilly promptly sneezed into it. I passed Mum a second linen square.

"Edith hasn't made up wedding invites since the 4th grade. What is this about your science exam?"

I shrugged, lifting the lid of the pot and giving the stew I found an experimental poke with my fork. "It was OK. I got a 'C'."

Mum put her hands on her hips, "That doesn't sound like the grade of a girl who might be chosen to represent her school in the national science fair."

I sat down and drummed my fingers against my plate. The surface flipped over and turned blue as the table decided it needed irradiating once more. I wiped my hands on my napkin.

"I didn't answer the section on why society has breeders and non-breeders."

Mum frowned. She dolled out a portion of stew onto Tilly's plate and handed her a fork.

"But you know all of that. In this day and age,

we can cure all these diseases that would previously have killed a person but ...."

"If we let them have children, then bad genes get given to babies," Tilly's voice chimed in with her kindergarten lessons. "And we want only the best genes for new babies. Then God and Mr Darwin are happy in heaven that we haven't messed up their way of making better humans through eva.... evo..... evi...."

"Evolution," I finished for her. "I know. I just didn't feel like answering the question, that's all." I busied myself with unnecessarily cutting Tilly's stew into smaller pieces.

I could feel Mum staring at me as I concentrated on the plate of meat and vegetables.

"Addy," her voice was surprisingly gentle. "You'd tell us if you were being bullied again, wouldn't you?"

I nodded, not looking up as I carefully dissected a lentil into four easy to eat parts.

"I'm not, really Mum. It's much better. People here are really nice."

People here just don't know. Tilly lifted her fork and dug it into her food. Its newly mushed form caused it to run through the prongs.

I looked up into my Mum's worried face and smiled brightly. "I will represent the school at the science fair," I told her. "I've got a good feeling about it."

◎

When my tablet started to vibrate in science class the following afternoon, I dropped it in surprise. It hit the desk and jiggled around so the whole room could see that I had received an official message from the school office. Faces turned towards me, grinning as I flushed red.

"I knew it would be you!" The girl sitting next to me elbowed my rib cage, beaming. "You better do us proud!"

I looked up at the front desk where our teacher was scanning the room for the source of the disruption.

"Miss? May I....?"

She smiled and nodded her assent.

"Yes, run along Addison and bring us back the news that a member of our class will be representing the school in the national science fair!"

Sliding from my seat, I left the room, forcing myself to keep my pace down to a brisk walk. I had tried to pretend to be indifferent, but imagining the look on Dad's face when I told him I had been chosen out of the entire school caused my mouth to turn up in a broad grin. I had never been selected for any honour at my last school.

Reaching the headmistress' office, I pressed my hand against the smooth metal panel above the door handle.

"Come in, Addison," the voice was accompanied by the door swinging inwards.

Unable to contain my enthusiasm, I took a big step inside to walk straight into the back of a man standing in front of the headmistress's desk. My view was obscured by orange teflon as he turned to look down at me. Hastily moving backwards, I turned my face up to see it reflected in the plastic of the hood that fitted over the man's head.

"Addison," the headmistress's voice was muffled through the mask of breathing apparatus that she had placed over her own mouth and nose. "You must be brave."

◎

Tilly looked very small lying on the hospital bed. If not for the board reading "Mathilda Lambeth" above her head, I might not even have recognised her beneath the streams of wires that were connected to her small chest.

I noticed that they had already tattooed her neck. The black ink was clearly visible even at this distance, unweakened by Dad's laboratory solution. My hand automatically rose to my own mark, barely visible unless you really looked for it.

In beds beside my younger sister were my mother, father and Edith. My parents waved tiredly from where they lay. Edith scowled at me, but her face looked so terribly afraid I did not have the heart to feel angry. Numbly, I turned from the closed ward's observation window to the medic standing beside me.

"Will they be all right?" My voice cracked.

A latex covered hand rested on my shoulder.

"We're doing everything we can." The medic's voice was soft, as if talking to the terminally ill. "Addison, we need to ask you .... did you not go home yesterday?"

I blinked up at him in surprise. "I went home after school."

The eyes studied me seriously behind the hazmat hood. "You're not in trouble." The voice remained low, quiet, friendly. "If you fell out with one of your sisters or wanted to hang out with friends ..... no one is going to reprimand you."

My expression turned angry. Why was I being questioned about silly fictitious arguments when my family were sick?

"No! I went home with Mum, Dad and Tilly last night. Edith went out." I turned back to gaze at my elder sister. "She was barely home at all." My voice dropped to a quieter note. None of this made sense. "So why is she sick and not me?"

The silence to my left lasted so long that I wrenched my eyes away from my family and up to the medic who was staring at me intently.

"Why indeed," he said.

◎

Tilly died at 0200 the next morning. I was not even allowed to see her in death; her body was immediately cremated in an attempt to contain the disease.

It failed.

I stared through the observation window, refusing to turn around at the squeak of a trolley being pushed behind me, the silence of its drivers a testament to its cargo. Gently, I raised a hand to tap on the glass pane. Mum did not turn to look at me, her eyes fixed unblinkingly on the place where Tilly's bed had stood. Edith ignored me too, but I could not rule out she was just in a sulk. She lay facing the opposite direction to Mum, her new black tattoo concealed by the pillow. Only Dad lifted an arm in my direction, but the motion had become worn down as the days had passed to more of a finger twitch than a wave. I did not know that tears poured down my face until the glass misted up before my eyes. One by one, the people I loved were obscured by the fog.

A hand, warm and reassuring, came down on my shoulder. I looked up into the familiar eyes of the medic who had brought me to the hospital. He had told me his name at least three times, but I had never managed to focus long enough to remember it. He did not seem to mind.

"Addison." His normally quiet voice was a bit louder than usual. For him, it almost sounded like uncontainable excitement. "We have some good news."

I stared at him blankly as if I did not know the words.

Reaching up, the medic unzipped the neck of his suit, breaking the air seal and lifting the hood clear of his head. "Really good news," he said, and smiled.

As we walked through the hospital, I kept my eyes fixed resolutely ahead, away from the wards and their occupants. The smell of disinfectant mingled with the continual background of stifled wailing, like static on an ancient radio.

The far wing of the hospital was laid aside for offices. Vinyl tiles gave way to carpet and the air took on a stagnant, disconnected odour. The door we were approaching was ajar, although the conversation from within was so loud this hardly made a difference.

"This is exactly why non-breeder labs should be locked!" The high pitched voice cracked through the air like a whip. "You treat the contents like a child's play room and now it could kill us all."

"Jessica." The second voice was pacifying. "The security was never necessary. By definition, the material stored there was what we were trying to arm the human race against. No one would take that for biological warfare."

"Mother nature took it for biological warfare!"

A woman, still incased in her sealed suit, came to the doorway as we approached. Her eyes curved like the angles on her horn rimmed glasses.

"Addison Lambeth." It was not a question. "Your family caused this, yet you may save us all. How ironic."

I stopped dead, heat rushing through my body like it had not done in days. Like it had not done since I saw the line of Tilly's heart monitor go flat.

"Excuse me?! You are accusing my baby sister, my dead baby sister of causing this .... this...." There were no words for this life.

"Ms Lambeth." The woman's companion came to the door and gestured us inside with a benevolent wave. "Jessica meant no such thing. She, like you, is deeply upset by what has occurred."

I pictured every single one of those beckoning fingers breaking.

"The virus has been traced to your father's lab." Jessica's words were an economical as her clipped tone. "Undoubtedly it was created through carelessness and then transmitted to your sister."

Daddy!
H-hey Tilly!

"Antidote?" my voice was cracked. "If you know the cause, you can make .... "

"No," Jessica cut me off. "We cannot. But you can."

They had lost their minds. I was FOURTEEN. I balled my hands into fists, ready to strike this warped woman with her sick idea of humour.

"You're immune." The hand of the medic was back on my shoulder, squeezing gently. "You held your sister the night she fell sick, but you didn't catch it. Even your older sister couldn't avoid it, although she was only home for a few minutes."

I looked up at him. He was smiling.

"We can use your stem cells to produce a vaccine."

The clock on the wall ticked once, twice, three times while I stared at the medics, at Jessica, and tried to understand. They could use my cells to find a cure. My parents would live. Edith would find a surrogate for the 17 kids she hoped to have with her latest boyfriend. He would probably run in panic and we would have to bring them up together. Mum and Dad could call twelve of them 'Tilly'. We would be a family again, not a disease.

"You can take the cells from my tissue?" I asked,

my voice a whisper that ached with hope.

"No, it must be embryonic," Jessica lifted a folder of notes and started to scan through what looked like a pile of lab results. "A single type will not do, even if they could divide fast enough."

My mouth turned dry and I licked my lips. I had to tell them. My medical notes were not yet on file, so they had to be working from my school registration form that said ....

"The non-breeder lab," I began. The eggs were there, not inside of me.

"Destroyed," Jessica did not even look up. "We could not take the risk of any material mutating into a different strain of this virus. We melted it down to the last test tube." She turned to look at me.

"Thank god you're a breeder," she said as she left.

LIST POEM
by Kristen McHenry

My mother was an oracle of lists,
careful scribe, each spell
of recall cast in ink and cursive.
In this way, nothing
was left behind, not
butter, not bras, not
apricots or gin. In this way, nothing
was left undone, neither beds
nor supper, bills nor braids.
She marked off the accounted for
with two stark, assertive lines.

My own lists unravel, tatters
of good intent forged
in invisible ink: Three Questions,
Four Agreements, Six
Habits, Seven Laws. To floss
each evening at sundown,
and never a carb after six.
To quiet the mind, to plant carrots
to wash the sheets more often.

To banish judgment and meet
each morning with a corpulent heart.

The joy is never in the execution
but in the crossing off, the banishment
of each righteous act, the sweet relief of
two hard lines, muffling the burden.

NOTES ON SURRENDER
by Kristen McHenry

We when we think
of surrender we think
of salmon, of their thoughtless yielding
to biology, and of those
poor saps in archaic tales,
forced to slaughter their own
to learn the nature of loss.

So forgive me but today I shredded
with my own hands each
of your bouquet's petals
just at the peak of their bloom. My fingers
stink of rose. I have wiped
their tribal stains onto my cheeks.
I did it, understand, because
I resented their timing,
unwilling as I was to bear
witness to their death--not this dozen,
not these.

How many has God lost

to our disregard for a mystery, to our
heroic, ham-handed
rescue of our ourselves?

Let us surrender this day to our cowardice, to our
one bad turn too many. Let fear
take hold of us completely, let us
offer it our necks.
It's okay for a while to cower
frozen in our terror,
to clench and hide,
until starving,
we emerge to search for home.

WINTER PEOPLE
by Kristen McHenry

It snowed and slowly I awoke, slowly I remembered
that I was born a winter person, born for adapting. I
remember now, that I have few but vital knowings:
*How to Protect from the Wind, How to Keep the Blood
Warmed in Freezing Conditions. How to adapt my eyes
to the dimness, how to become, in fact, intolerant of light.*
And my essential nature--how my skin shrinks
from the breath of the sun, how my skin is not: nut-
brown, light-craving, healed by heat. How I was
born fighting against the elements, how it changes
you when you're delivered at birth into the shock of
wind chill and deep frozen white, when you must
choose early and wisely your methods of survival,
when you are weaned on tales of frostbite and the
lengths others before you have gone to keep from
dying of cold. It changes you, to know that you
must always carry with you the tools of survival:
Always, matches in a waterproof tin. Always, a
blade with which to stab your prey. Always, a fur to
protect the heart. Always a willingness to kill that
which you love, so you may plunge your raw hands

into their still-warm viscera, so you may be granted
another twenty, invaluable minutes of warmth.
And of course, the skills needed to build a fire in
the wilderness, in the dead of winter, everything
hostile and incurably damp.

◎

When I dream, I dream of summer people. What it
is like to be dusky, to require the heat. To be born in
sun, to be born knowing the land will always warm
you, that the land wrapped you in itself from the
moment you entered the world. That as a newborn,
you looked straight into the white, roaring sun,
and from then on your eyes were ready, eager,
expectant of love.

MANIFESTO
by Kristen McHenry

The world stands perfectly still.
The world hasn't moved an inch in weeks.
Crows have gone under, dreaming
that Spring lies limpid in their beaks. Earth
is off the hook entirely.
We shall expect
nothing of it. What's required now,
my friends,
is scarves—not for their warmth
but for their brilliance: Lime and
scarlet, fire and turquoise,
coral, fuchsia and polished plum, plumage
fanned around our pallid necks, its dazzle
meant to send a message
in no uncertain terms:

We will not
ourselves go bald and
rigid as the trees. We will not be frozen out.
We will explode against the deadened
backdrop of these times, marching

through the gray wind
bearing our floppy,
luminous gems. We will be fearless.
We will show the winter that our colors
have been at last reclaimed—
that we do indeed,
remember gaudy Summer,
its mesmerizing hues.

OLDER
by Fernando A. Flores

older by the paycheck
by the heartache
older by the stack of
corks and beercans
by the books you've read
cars you've crashed
dogs you've buried
older by immunization
by another winter's cold
popped pimpled and erased
journal entries, burned
love letters and cigarettes
older by aching teeth
and cuts from the razor
imagined bumps under arm
pits or balls or tits
older by skipped meals
receipts in your pocket
another business card
discarded sofa and mattress
torn socks and underwear

and toxic toilet paper
older by another forgotten writer
and newly paved streets
with bad digestion and
mysterious red freckles
replacing flat tires
talking yourself out of
another drink another love
another west coast fire
capped oil well, older by
another nobel, pulitzer,
academy award ceremony,
blown out candles and marriage
older by design by luck
thinking of all the dead
older than vesper hymns
abandoned coal and diamond
mines with buried workers
and black and red cadillacs
down this here interstate
and controlled grass fires
older than our fathers and
thursday night hail marys.

MR THOMAS
by Ruth Solomon

Mr Thomas carried the cake under his arm in a
wooden box. In the front of the box was a small
window so that passers by could, if they wished,
look in and see the cake. When Mr Thomas got to
the iron fence at the edge of the park he took the
metal chain and padlock, threaded it though a metal
ring that was attached to the box and then wound
the chain around a bar on the iron fence. Finally he
locked the padlock with a key which he took from
his trouser pocket. Then he walked home across the
park.

The following morning Mr Thomas walked
back through the park. It was a beautifully clear
morning. Dew was on the grass. A bird was singing
loudly. When he reached the fence the wooden box
containing the chocolate cake had disappeared and
so had the iron bar to which it had been attached.
Mr Thomas carried another identical wooden
box under his arm also with a window through
which a chocolate cake would be seen. Mr Thomas
diligently secured it to the iron bar next to the one

that had been removed. For the next month, the same activity occurred. Each night the little box containing the cake together with the iron bar of the fence was removed. The following morning a new cake was attached to the next bar along. Finally by the end of the month the fence was completely gone.

Mr Thomas found the time to take a vacation. Somewhere where there was no cooking to be done.

When Mr Thomas returned from holiday he went back to work immediately for there were plenty of other fences in the park that needed attention. But the very next morning when he went down to the iron fence to inspect his work with yet another cake-box tucked under his arm he was compelled to go directly to the police.

"Officer" he said.

"Someone has smashed the glass on my new wooden cake box and they've simply removed the cake".

"Vandalism" said the officer and shrugged. Mr Thomas no longer works in the park. That incident has upset him.

DYSLEXIC PASSION

THE GRANDMA TREE
by Louise Tondeur

My grandmother liked knitting and she made me
wind her wool up for her in tight balls. Before the
kitten drowned, it liked to chase my grandmother's
wool across the floor. Sometimes different colours,
green, blue, pink, purple, would criss-cross each
other from the kitten-wool game if my sister had
been playing for a long time. It depended what my
grandmother was making. If she made something
multi-coloured, and my sister played for a long
time, then it would happen. Once, my grandmother
made me a stripy scarf that went all the way down
to the floor. Another time, she made me a jumper
to go with the scarf. When she was doing that the
wool went too and fro across the floor in a giant
Technicolor spider's web. I wound it up carefully
afterwards. I didn't mind doing it. I liked it. The
fire jumped around excitedly. My grandmother's
needles went click click click. My sister held the
kitten to the window so she could watch the snow
falling. I could smell dinner simmering in the
kitchen. I wound the wool back up tight into balls

and arranged them in her knitting bag, like jumper seeds ready to spring into life.

My grandmother would sit in the kitchen with me sometimes while I drank milk and took bites out of my sandwich so they made a pretty pattern. She put her arm around me and said she was going to tell me a story. Her stories would always start in the place where we were. If we were in the garden, under the oak tree, that's where it would start. Once there were two birds sitting in an oak tree. If we were by the pond, that's where it would start. Once, there were seven sisters who sat and sewed by a shinning silver pond. If we happened to be strolling through the garden and kicking the leaves with our feet, it would begin there. Once two boys shuffled through the leaves and ate baked potatoes as they walked. Or: Once there were seven sisters who stood in the autumn wind and played with each other's hair. Sometimes it started in the kitchen.

"I knew a woman who told me about a girl who liked to sit at her kitchen table all day long," my grandmother said. She put her arm around me when she told her stories. Her arm told the story as well. If it got frightening, she would hold me tighter. If there was a storm on a boat, she would rock me to and fro. If there was a wishing well, she would move her hand to my shoulder and we would pretend to look into the well together to make our wish and wait to see if it came true. If two people fell in love, she would stroke my elbow and gaze into the distance as if she was remembering the time she fell in love with my grandfather. That was in a field. I knew because she had told me about lying on her back in the grass. Her arm was like a thick rope binding me to the tale.

◎

I had a crush on the gardener's daughter. She had blonde hair and a turned up nose and she sat cross-legged under the window, next to the dog roses. I leant against the oak tree, sewing beads onto my purse and watched her. I liked her blue eyes. They shone whenever she looked at me. She gave me an earthy feeling, or rather, a turned up earth feeling, like someone was digging there, turning me over. I sat down next to her and crossed my legs too. She looked at me solemnly and didn't say anything at first. She just dug around in the earth with a stick.

"See the oak tree?"

"Yes," I said.

"I bet I can hang from that branch by my knees, with no hands."

"OK then," I said. She checked to make sure her father wasn't looking, ran over to it, climbed quickly and hung from the strongest branch, upside down, her hair falling towards the ground, her arms dangling, her t-shirt falling over her face. I watched. After a while, she righted herself and ran back over.

"Does it hurt?" I said.

"A bit," she said and shrugged. After that, we gazed up into the branches together and they criss-crossed over our heads. Then I heard my middle sister coming and for some reason I didn't want her to know we were there, so I pulled my new friend behind the tree trunk. No-one could see us anyway, the branches hung down towards the earth like a skirt. The gardener's daughter giggled as we watched my middle sister's feet go past. I suddenly felt happy, being next to her and next to the trunk of the oak. All summer, we lay under the branches of the old oak together and looked up at the criss-cross roof above us. One day we were lying on our backs and it was cold. She gave me her jumper and

I draped it over both of us, so it was like we were in bed together. I thought it was funny.

"What?" she said.

"Nothing," I said. I was embarrassed.

"I'm going away," she said, suddenly. I sat up so I was leaning on my elbows.

"Why?" I said.

"For gardening school. My Dad's sending me."

"How far away?" I said.

"I don't know. A long way." She dug in her pocket like she was digging in the earth and pulled out a silver sphere on a long chain. She held my hand and pressed it into my palm.

"What is it?"

"Open it," she said. I did as she told me. I lifted the lid and watched as a needle bobbed over a curling N for North. A compass.

"To show you the way," she said.

I cried when she left. It felt, not like a friend leaving, but like I had lost my arm or my tongue or my foot. I had that same phantom sense that the lost thing was still there, haunting me.

◎

My pet guinea pig died on the day you left. My

father told me and my six sisters to bury it in the muddy patch beyond the oak tree. I wrapped the small black body in cloth and laid it in the grave. As I watched my eldest sister cover it over, I cried and they thought I was crying for my pet, but I wasn't. I was frightened that a tree would grow up on the spot where we had planted her, a whole tree of guinea pigs, which would start out as giant black and brown flowers and blossom into squeaking furry bundles wrapped in see through silky leaves, waiting to fall like apples did. How frightening it would be to stand under the tree and listen to the squeaking. But though I waited, and looked out of the window, at the fallen brown leaves, at the snow and the hard ground, at the new green buds, the guinea pig tree didn't grow. Even though I had been frightened, I watched even harder, for longer, because I thought that maybe watching made it happen.

One night, when it got truly dark, and everyone else was in bed, I crept outside. I knelt down near to, but not quite next to, where my pet guinea pig lay, put my hands into the dark earth and let it crumble between my fingers. Then I dug a bit deeper. I scooped out a whole handful and then

another and another until I had a hole. Quickly, I
dipped my hand into my pocket and pulled out
the purse I had made myself out of soft pink cloth
and coloured beads. The beads made a spiral
pattern like a wave across the surface in blue and
white. I watched the wave for a while, but I didn't
press my fingers to it like I wanted to because they
were caked in earth from digging. I held the purse
carefully trying not to get it muddy. All the same,
when I opened the clasp, I left two fingerprints
either side like I had committed a crime. I took out
the silver compass you gave me from inside and
settled it in the hole I had made. Then I covered it
with the soil I had disturbed.

◉

One day in Spring my eldest sister found me behind
a curtain and asked me why I was hiding. I couldn't
tell her about the guinea pig tree or the compass
tree that I might find growing one day below my
window with black flowers blowing in the wind, or
humming silver berries. I let her sit in the window
seat and hold onto me, and I cried into her shoulder.
After that, I didn't watch anymore. I felt as if I had
changed, like some girls change from playing with

dolls to suddenly throwing their dolls down the
stairs. I had changed from a girl who watches for
a guinea pig or a compass trees to someone else,
a new person, as if I had been buried in the earth
myself and now I was shooting up through the soil,
pushing up my green fingers, reaching up so my
chin and mouth and nose broke the surface, taking
a breath, admiring my own trunk. I couldn't have
spoken about it then, but I knew it inside, like a tree
must know that it's a tree inside its trunk, because
it doesn't have a head to think with. I never told
anyone about it. It sunk deep into the bit of me
that would have been my trunk if I had been a tree
myself.

◎

I got a sharp guilty kick in the stomach, from the
inside, the first time my sister suggested that we
plant a tree, like I was remembering a guilty secret.
Like the time when I ate three shortcake biscuits
under the covers in the middle of the night. It was
like that, when I remembered planting my pet
guinea pig and the compass. I was a bit older and
taller. My eldest sister had a baby by then. I was an
auntie and a godmother.

"Why don't we plant a tree?" she said.

"So the baby can watch it grow." I wondered how she knew about planting trees, because I hadn't told anyone at all. I hadn't even whispered it into my pillow at night.

My middle sister had a kitten which drowned in the pond. She said that the kitten's ghost slept on her pillow, but I said she was stupid because ghosts don't have to sleep. The kitten that drowned sunk under the water, right down to where the weeds are. We saw its nose and its eyes and then its ears go under. We waited to see if it would fight its way back to the surface, but it didn't; it sunk like a stone. I wondered if my sister watched the pond to see if kitten water lilies would spread across the surface, just like I watched for the guinea pig tree and the compass tree, but I didn't think about it much at all, because it was her kitten and so they would be her water lilies. Anyway. We didn't plant the kitten. It sunk all by itself. I wasn't sure if things grew if you hadn't planted them.

Just after the kitten drowned in the pond, that spring, when the waters were swollen, my grandmother died on the sofa with her knitting needles in her hands. My father decided that she would be buried in the gardens. My sister came to stay with her baby so that she could organise it. She called the priest and the gravediggers and the stonemasons, and ordered wandering flowers around the edges of the stone and much loved mother and grandmother for the words. That was when my sister suggested the tree again. That evening we were sitting on the sofa where my grandmother had died. My sister held up an acorn she had found in the garden, under the oak tree, which my father said was four hundred years old.

"Do you know what this is?" she said. She showed it to the baby as well as me, so I wasn't sure who she was talking to at first. Of course I knew what it was.

"It's an acorn," I said. My sister jigged the baby on her hip. I looked at its bald head and tiny fingers and remembered that I was a fairy godmother and one day I would have to turn pumpkins into coaches. I wondered how I was going to manage it.

"If you look really really carefully, you can see the oak tree curled up inside it, waiting to come out." I took it in my hand and looked. I couldn't see the tree at all, but I just nodded anyway.

"I can see it," I said.

"When we have the priest come to put grandma to sleep in the earth, shall we put the acorn in too?" my sister said.

"Then she can grow into a big tree. As big as the old tree at the bottom of the garden, that you can hide under." I looked at her sharply. I got the inside kick in my stomach. I imagined watching a tree grow from my bedroom window. In the spring, big white flowers would grow, with multicoloured balls of wool for berries around them. Then in the summer, the flowers would turn into grandmas, wrapped in cotton, ready to fall.

"A grandma tree?" I said. My sister smiled, took the acorn back, and put it in her pocket.

"Yes," she said.

Nothing happened all summer. Through the autumn the grave with the grey stone was covered in brown leaves. In the winter it turned white as grandma's hair. In March, I saw something from my bedroom window. I ran down into the garden before anyone else was up. The grandma tree had started to grow. I watched it all year long. I sat next to it when the first leaves were unfolding like tiny hands. I felt the thin trunk, which was thinner than my little finger. I phoned my sister. The baby was starting to walk now. I could hear her crying in the background.

"The grandma tree has leaves now," I said.

"Good. I'll come over and see it later. Have the others seen it?"

"No," I said.

"Good. It can be our secret for now, until they find it for themselves." It was our secret until, one by one, my sisters found the new tree. I watched them from my bedroom window. They went one at a time, when they remembered that Grandma wasn't on the sofa anymore, to look at the stone. It was still cold and their breath sung around their heads as they looked. Two, three, four, five, six. Two knelt to pray. She was religious, but she didn't mind who she prayed to. She prayed to fairies and clouds and trees. Three with a candle, which the wind kissed out. Four with a ball of wool which she wound around her hand like a rosary. It was the one she kept under her pillow for the dead kitten to play with. Five with a storybook which she read from early in the morning, and six, who ran back for a watering can. We never visited the tree at the same time. We had our unspoken days. Monday, Tuesday, Wednesday, Thursday, Friday.

My eldest sister, who had her baby on her hip, and I were one and seven. Sometimes on a Saturday we stood together, reading the words on the stone, and watching the grandma tree grow. Sometimes on Sundays, I went on my own.

One Sunday night when the world was quiet, I stood watching the grandma tree from my bedroom window. I imagined grandma below pushing up through the soil, reaching up an arm, pushing with her head, straining her fingers, wriggling until she could feel herself being sucked up into the roots and pushing up into the thick trunk. But it wasn't ready for her yet. So grandma was waiting, I thought, just under the soil, until the trunk and the branches got thick enough to hold her, then she would climb up and sit inside. Then she would push an arm into each branch. She would grow extra arms so she could feel a bit of her inside each one. She would grow extra fingers so she would be in every leaf. But that wouldn't be for a very long time, a hundred years maybe, I thought to myself, until the trunk was thick enough. Just then I noticed, glinting in the moonlight, a bush had grown up around the grandma tree for a skirt. It had silver-white branches like fingers of ice. I ran downstairs, and out into the garden. I knelt in front of the silver bush. At the end of each branch were tiny seedpods. I pressed one of them between my thumb and finger, and out fell a silver sphere, tiny, pea-shaped, with a hinged lid. I opened it. I listened carefully. I could hear my guinea pig squeaking like a ghost when I lifted it to my ear.

When I looked over my shoulder, you were waiting for me in the middle of the frosty grass. You were grown up, but your hair was still in a bob and your nose was still turned up at the edges.

"Hello," you said. You looked at me with shiny blue eyes.

"My grandma died and now she's growing into a tree," I said. You thought about it.

"That's good," you said. I stood up and took your hand.

A BRIEF PHASE OF HEDONISM
by Abs Watson

He's got tabs of acid in his fridge, wrapped in tin
foil
Takes a massive slug of ket in the morning before
kissing me on the neck
Tender, soft and fresh out of the shower
With white frosty nostrils; an avalanche backwards.

The mornings were always the best and the worst,
A tiger in my tummy and a bull in my brain
The smell of sex on the sheets with substances in his
pockets
Eyeliner on pillows and lies to my mother.

He once punched someone in the face for pushing
me to the ground in a mosh pitBought me a book
for my twentieth birthday
Says 'a fink a love yer' as I lie with greasy hair
Trying to wiggle my way out of the current
conversation

We'd get off the train; you'd head straight for the

pub
Whilst I walked home in the sun, smelling like
musk

For I'm too small for goodness,
But I think that you were too.
And for a while it was well
And was all that I wanted to do

And you may not have been the best for me,
But for those summer months
You offered me something exciting
Than was more than just your drugs

Not a waster, or a wanker,
Just someone wanting more
But for me it was enough
Me, you and your mattress on the floor.

JUST SADLY THERE
by Fernando A. Flores

blue stockings
over my shoulders
in a hot, damp room
with no ceiling fan
and moaning wallpaper
peeling against us
in west texas
lifting up, kissing,
making me feel good
while I make you come
there is never a symphony
playing when there needs
to be, only peaches
and abandoned vineyards
deep inside you against
me wet in west texas,
shaking like a freight train
or a frightened lamb
under the acne scarred moon,
surrendered, see the sun
in your fever, burning

down the sheets,
flooding the walls,
shrieks after a bad dream,
the rapture of it all,
I peel off your blue
stockings, drink up your sweat
thinking of checkout bills,
gambling with no protection,
the next day forgetting
the blue stockings, picturing
them just sadly there
in the room as we drive
away, never south, never
east, north, especially
never back west, the highway
spread in front of me
like your unshaved legs, vanishing

THE MISTRESS
by Nicola Fawley

Hidden in the shadows of branches
Her leathery scales change to suit her mood
A Male captivated by her colours
She creeps towards him, pausing

Swivelling eyes fixed upon him
She waits; legs and tail stretched
A flick of her tongue she strikes
Mitten claws grip him tight

Mouth wide; she projects a bitter hiss
Sunburst skin glows and he retreats
Her colours dim and legs shuffle
Returning to the branches she hides

PETER PARMINTER
by Andy Thatcher

A Devon field seems an unlikely place to come
across a burned out shopping centre, yet every
morning for a year, after drawing the curtains,
I awoke to just that. I suspect it may have been
why the property was so cheap, was what made
it possible for me to relocate from a London
flat cramped with the effects of six decades to
somewhere more fitting to recuperate from
the blood-letting exercise that was my second
divorce. No one in Chumleigh seemed to want to
talk about the shopping centre should I ask, not
beyond mentioning the terrible fire followed by a
sorrowful, respectful shaking of the head. Not the
postman, nor The Weary Ploughman's landlord,
nor the girls at the deli, not even the estate agent
who had shown me round the cottage in the first
place.

   I didn't meet my neighbours for some time,
though after some weeks I did get to meet their
teenage grandson who appeared to live there
on and off. I was measuring for a garden office

one afternoon. He was on the other side of the fence, prodding at the dirt with a hoe, sucking at a hand-rolled cigarette, earphones in. He was as thin as his hoe, in glaring white Adidas, his skin the colour of the ash he was dropping. He caught my eye, grunted and kept on hoeing to his music, looking up maliciously every once in a while until he paused, leaning on the hoe and staring at me, earphones still in. I attempted to say hello. He made a face of irked incomprehension. I attempted another hello and the earphones came out. A final hello and I got another grunt. I asked after the burned-out shopping centre and that seemed to do the trick. I paraphrase here as the grandson delivered the following in a studied drawl which overlaid a deeply fruity West Country accent with an approximation of inner city London, carefully-stocked with the likes of nuff, lak a say and izzit. That said, the lad nevertheless told the story with more pace and verve than I'd heard in months.

Duff's Farm Shopping Village had catered for vem uptown peeps. One could shop there for artisan cobblestones or award-winning Gruyere, one could learn ayervedic pilates or carbon-neutral chicken-husbandry (these details courtesy of an evening's googling through old adverts over a bottle of rioja.) Vem uptown peeps came from miles around like exotic bees to a traditionally crafted honeypot. On a busy summer's Saturday, the smell of facial moisturiser could apparently drift for miles.

The fire had broken out in the deli's rotisserie on the day before Mother's Day. According to the grandson, three had died in the blaze, including Mr. Duff himself, and quite a few shoppers were injured, overcome by the fumes of burning truffle oil. The fire also destroyed Little Devon, a model village and garden of rest that had stood on the adjoining site for more than forty years. Sparks from the main inferno ignited the thatch on a thicket of miniature cottages and this scaled down blaze spread to Exeter Cathedral, Okehampton Castle, Hound Tor and Dartmoor Prison. The ash turned the sea to soup at Dartmouth, Salcombe, Bideford and Ilfracombe. The water in the carefully blue-painted Dart and Taw and Exe became steam.

Though stating quite plainly not to be personally inclined towards gossip, the lad hinted that mystery surrounded the destruction of Little Devon, which had finally closed its gates to the public the previous day, since when nothing had been seen of its owner, Peter Parminter, who was locally renowned for his mutton-chops sideburns.

Proper freaky geezer, 'im said the grandson.

Shortly after the death of his wife, the then-young Parminter constructed a model church at the bottom of his garden to hold her ashes. A post office, cottages and a farm went on to join it over the following year. For a few pence, Peter Parminter would let the curious have a look round. Then, on the fifth anniversary of Mrs. Parminter's death, he bought an adjoining field and Little Devon and Garden of Rest was established in earnest.

Proper freaky likkle 'stablishment, vat said the grandson, as did the clutch of Chumleigh's locals who would be drawn on the matter, though using rather different diction.

And yet scores of retirees who, for their twilight years, had traded the hurly-burly for rural Devon, coughed up good money for the chance to have their ashes scattered, for a commemorative plaque, for a hand-painted figure of themselves to be added to the village. But tastes in the scattering of ashes change, as do the habits of tourists, as does Health and Safety legislation and Peter Parminter had struggled financially during the five years leading up to the Duff's Farm blaze. When that took place, Parminter was, so it was said, on the point of selling Little Devon to the Duff family for the building of a new car park but then the grandson reiterated that he wasn't inclined towards gossip, and that seemed to bring the conversation to an abrupt halt.

I commented on the attractiveness of his grandfather's Busy Lizzies, he commented on the plans for my well wicked shed and we went our separate ways. I had spent two hours digging this information out of the grandson and went on to do my best to uncover more, but the police report was late in appearing and even the web was curiously taciturn on the matter, as if it, too, shook its head saying terrible fire. There were no articles on local press sites, no tribute Facebook pages, no Youtube conspiracy theories. It was most perplexing.

◉

Spring gave way to summer and, my garden office built, I decided it would be neighbourly to have a barbeque. Old Bob, the granddad, who I'd at last met, seemed keen and said Maureen, his vole of a wife, might even put in an appearance. I invited the girls at the deli, The Weary Ploughman's landlord and a few old-timers who lived at its bar. Then my thoughts turned to my other neighbour.

The grandson had warned me that Eve was well bonkers. A sculptor and a blown-in like myself, she lived in a converted barn at the end of a deeply rutted lane. Other than her old Volvo rattling up and down or the occasional waft of wood polish or stewed pulses, she might not have even lived there. Her garden certainly gave that impression.

Eve was eating couscous in the sun when I arrived. She was guardedly grateful to receive her invitation, but hunched over the couscous as if I might make a lunge for it. As an icebreaker, I opened the discussion of the blaze at Duff's Farm and the couscous was pushed aside, Eve's eyes all lit up like a petrol station forecourt.

Had anyone told me that Peter Parminter's wife had been Duff-the-elder's sister and that they had fallen out over the business with the ashes? No, she didn't think so. Yes, and the better Duff's Farm and Little Devon did for themselves, the deeper grew the rift. And after Duff-the-elder died and Duff the Younger moved back to start up the Shopping

Village, it had been the latter Duff who reported
to Environmental Health, who had tipped off the
Inland Revenue, who went on to offer Old Mutton
Chops well under the going rate for the land. And
wasn't it interesting that Duff the Younger had died
in the fire?

And doubtless no one had said about the
unexplained, teeny-tiny marks on the rotisserie?
Had I heard that the fire exits were welded shut?
That both shoppers and firemen witnessed bottles
of truffle oil being thrown at the blaze? And there
was nothing hallucinogenic about those fumes,
that was just a cover up, just like the delay on the
report. But everyone knew because everyone had
heard the stories. And it was why everyone ignored
her, now. Because Eve – and she knew they all
called her Bonkers Eve – just wouldn't hold her
tongue.

I said good day to my neighbour and fervently
hoped she would come to believe the barbeque a
conspiracy to have her conveniently disappeared.
Whether that was the case or not, she did not come,
as neither did the girls at the deli, the landlord or
the old timers. All that hand-reared meat and those
seasonal leaves were lavished on the grandson who

stayed precisely eight minutes and would doubtless
have been more at home with a bucket meal from
KFC. Eve never so much as caught my eye again.

◎

My old partner-in-crime Simon visited at the end
of the summer, in the mood to celebrate/ escape/
rub my nose in the birth of his sixth child. I let him
talk me into surfing. I let him talk me into vodka
cocktails. I talked his way out of several fights. And
on the final evening of his stay, I let him talk me into
breaking into the ruins of the model village, which
he had been badgering me to do since his arrival.
We hopped the fence as lithely as we could and took
a look.

Summer had been kind to Little Devon whereas
Duff's Farm looked more decrepit as its skeleton
continued to collapse, all remaining windows
long since smashed by Lower Chumleigh's ASBO
colony, with which I suspected the grandson
had affiliations. And though Peter Parminter's
bungalow had met with a similar fate to the
Shopping Village, new grass now grew on
Dartmoor's black stubble, rain had replenished
the Exe and Dart and Taw and had washed the ash

from beaches and harbours. New leaves sprouted from the scorched miniature shrubs.

However, rain and sun could not account for the resurrection of Exeter Cathedral or of Castle Drogo, which, though still scorch-marked in places, had their geometry, restored with minutely careful, neat handiwork. Neither could it account for the pristine thatch on the cottages, the fresh colours on the tiny cars. And though Okehampton Castle was still in ruins – wasn't it that way anyway?

Most fully restored of all was the church, the most senior of all the models. The grass around it was a deep green and looked trimmed, though most likely this was simply rabbits about their work. And right around the door to the church, where Mrs. Parminter's ashes were housed, was a great congregation of all the villages figures, hundreds of four-inch-high memorials to Devon's retirees, all smartly painted and facing the great church door where stood a bride and a groom with mutton-chop sideburns.

CHEESEHEAD
by Kristen McHenry

Go ahead, judge me. Just remember that at some
point in your tidy life of dry-cleaned suits and
pristine credit, you too, will know desperation. I
was like you once - a cocky son of bitch, a hotshot,
an up-and-comer, sure I was going to get everything
I wanted. That was before Garrett, before Misty, and
before Fabiano's grand re-opening in Mac's Famous
Food Mart. Before I ended up in this hellhole, where
the "cheese" consists of oily slabs of dye-injected
milk fat. It's such an insult to humanity I wouldn't
wish on my worst enemy, Garrett Deever, who I
blame for everything.

It started with money problems. The artisan cheese
business was slow. There's only so much you can
produce when you're working on a five-by-two
counter in an apartment kitchenette. And ever
since the DIY crowd got wind that cheese-making
would boost their hipster cred, they all started
getting in on it and flooding the market. They got a
lock on the local farmers' market, which wouldn't
let me hock my wares. That crap about having

an unlicensed kitchen was just a bullshit excuse.
They're threatened by a real man who knows his
art and can execute a Gruyère that makes the ladies
scream. I know for a fact that those bearded pansies
never made cheese in their lives. They pick it up
from Running River Farms in their Suburus and tell
the chicks they spent years cultivating the Asiago.

So when I read that Mac's Famous Food Mart
gutted its specialty cheese kiosk and leased the
space to Fabiano's - the Fabiano's - I had to get in.
I had thirty-eight dollars in the bank. My last batch
of Vlad's Virile Dill Havarti went bad when the
mercury hit 93 degrees on the same day my cheap
fridge died. I had to earn some scratch fast. Besides,
Fabiano's needed me if they were going emerge
from the flaming wreckage left by Mac's, a piss-ant
operation run by mouth-breathing college students
who didn't know a Stracchino from a Neufchâtel.
That wouldn't fly at Fabiano's. They hired the best,
and I was it. I've been studying cheese since I was
three years old in my mama's kitchen. Sure, I didn't
start making it until a few years ago, but experience
means squat when you're born with a gift.

It turned out Fabiano's hand-picked their staff
before they even started planning their grand

opening. And their star player was none other than Garrett Deever, the prettiest of all of the pretty boys, a baby-faced Swede with big blue eyes who turned all the ladies into babbling idiots. I'd hated Garrett ever since he was featured in Curds and Whey with his big, blond, extended family posing around his mother's rustic farmhouse in Jönköping, where they handcraft cheese for their family business. Look, I don't give a damn if some hack wants to ride on his family's coattails, but I draw the line at using mass media to tell the world microwaving mozzarella curd starts is "fine". No self-respecting artisan would microwave the curd. You dip the curd in progressively hotter water so you don't scorch it, and temper it using a salt water brine. But Garrett suddenly decided he was an expert because a bunch of photographers were sucking up to him.

When I read the article, I fired off an e-mail to the editor. He published it on their site, and within hours, it blew up all over the online cheese-making community. Garrett managed to get everyone on his side and make me look like the asshole. I have my own following, but when this shit went down, a lot my readers started following his blog instead of mine. On top of it, he had the gall to humiliate me

by starting a Tumblr with some drunk photos of me
he dredged up on Facebook, posting quotes from
our argument next to the pictures. When I told him
to take it down he insisted it wasn't his. But I know
damn well he was posting under a pseudonym. A
baby-face and an accent may fool some people, but
I know the real Garrett - a smarmy pit viper on the
take. He was even diabolical enough to post a plea
on his blog that whoever started the Tumblr take it
down because "we're all one artisan family".

Garrett Deever was in for a world of hurt. But first
I had to get myself onto Fabiano's payroll. When I
applied, it was a no-go. They had their crew, and
even when I went over my resume with them in
detail, they wouldn't make a place for me. Espresso
Monkey, the coffee stand across from Fabiano's,
was hiring, and they recognized a quality
candidate. I had pulled a few shots at Happy
Bean in my time, and I knew my way around a
macchiato. They put me on swing shift five days
a week. Fabiano's was an open kiosk twenty steps
away from Espresso Monkey. It was agony to be
so close, but at least I could keep an eye on Garrett
Deever and correct their staff when they gave
misinformation to a customer. It wouldn't take long

for them to notice my talent and hire me on.

It would be a fast climb to management, and after a few years, I'd have enough scratch saved to open my own shop. Then, the world would know who I was, and by that time Garrett Deever would be lucky to have a job wrapping Kraft cheese slices on an assembly line. I didn't even mind the humiliation of slumming it at Coffee Monkey because I knew it was short-term.

Coffee Monkey staffed two people to a shift, so it was easy to get away. My co-worker was Nim, a chunky, blue-haired art student who was willing to keep her mouth shut about my time at Fabiano's if I let her skim the tips. My first day on the job, they still had their grand opening banner up, and of course they trotted Garrett out to flirt and offer free samples to women. I watched this sickening tableau for a while before I left Nim and walked over to get a closer at look at their featured Blues. They'd gotten their hands on some prime stuff: Bleu d'Auvergne, Bleu de Laqueuille, Bleu de Septmoncel, even Bleu Des Causses. I couldn't afford it on a barista's wage, but a man can look.

Then Garrett Deever himself slimed up next to me with a platter of Moncenisio. "Peace offering?" he said, thrusting the cheese at me.

I didn't want to take his product, but it was Moncenisio. I grabbed a chunk, ate it, then took another. As much as it burned my hide, pretending to make nice with Garrett was a better strategy than open conflict.

"Thanks," I said.

Garrett set the tray down. "Listen, I thought you got a raw deal with all that mozzarella silliness. I understand your way. It is a good way."

I seethed at him for calling the conflict "silliness" when it's at the core of a battle for the very soul of artisan cheese making. But I kept my mouth shut. "Forget it. Water under the bridge."

Garrett grinned. "We good?"

"We're good." We did the dude handshake and I took another piece of cheese. "Sweet gig you got here," I said.

Garrett nods. "Fabiano's is top notch. I will soon have an apprenticeship."

"Yeah?" Of course, he'd manage to smarm his way into an apprenticeship. It was probably with Bernard Brosseau, who contracts with Fabiano's once a year to grace their star employees.

"With Monsieur Brosseau, of course! Can you

believe? I am a very lucky man, Vladimir."

"Yeah, congrats. So, when are you guys going to be hiring around here again?"

Infuriatingly, Garrett shrugged. "Only when someone quits. And so few quit Fabiano's. We get health insurance!"

I knew that. And I knew the staff because I had taken their names from Fabiano's website and run searches. Rebecca Rhodes, formerly of Rhodes farms in Vermont, Whitney Soames, Edwardo Bianco, Martin Dubois, Antoine Bonnet, and Ansel Graak. Whitney was a Le Cordon Bleu graduate, Edwardo was the son of a famous local restaurateur, Martin's family owned Dubois Farms in Minnesota, and Ansel ran the blog "Curdious" about his cheesemaking exploits with his Mormon girlfriend. The only mystery was Antoine. He didn't even show up in a Google search.

None of them were going to leave Fabiano's. Martin had two kids and Whitney was single and pregnant. Edwardo just bought a high-end condo, and Ansel was about to propose. Rebecca and Antoine were beginners trying to get their careers off the ground. They all had a stake in sticking around for a long time.

As Garrett stood gloating next to his tray of del Moncenisio, a woman approached - a saucy stunner in a vintage sundress, with legs a man would kill to glance at, big green eyes, and glossy brown hair cut in a Louise Brooks crop. I dropped the toothpick that I'd been holding and tried not to stare at her. She was wearing a weird necklace of beaded wires that made her even sexier.

"Excuse me?" She had that sort of breathy girl-voice that makes a man want to lift a car over his head. Garrett practically tripped over his wing-tips to get to her. He shoved himself between us and edged me out of the way.

"Yes, madam?" he asked, pasting on a sleazy grin. "Can I help you? We are sampling a lovely blue from the Piedmont region of Northern Italy."

Her nose wrinkled. "I don't know. I usually stick to cheddar."

"You must try," said Garrett, handing her a sample. "You will fall in love, I guarantee."

She took a tiny bite from the cube of cheese, paused, then finished the rest of it in one gulp. When I saw her face glow with pleasure, I fell in love. This woman, this cheese-naif, had it. Taste. Potential. She was green, but she could be taught. I could mold her, no pun intended, into a connoisseur.

"Oh, my goodness, it's heaven!" she said. "May I have one more? I've hardly eaten a bite all day."

"You may have as many as you wish, Madame." Garrett winked at her.

"That's good, but if you want the Cadillac of blues, you need to try this little beauty here." I whipped a wheel of Bleu de Septmoncel from the display and worked off the wrapper. "Smell that," I told her. "Close your eyes and take a deep whiff. What you got yourself there is a hint of nut and cream; but with an edge. A rebel soul."

"Mm." She smiled. My forehead was sweaty and something was wrong in my chest; a thudding pain that was making it hard for me to stand upright. I fought it down. I was Vlad Bardzecki the Second. I was confident. Chicks dig confidence. You go all weak-kneed in front of them, they lose respect.

"You like that," I said. "You're in tune with it. You got a little edge too, don't you?"

She blushed.

"Garrett, the lady would like a sample. Crack this baby open and give her a taste."

Garrett looked confused. "Olin didn't authorize us

to use that for samples."

"So? You're gonna let the man tell you she can't have a taste? "

Garrett smiled and took the Septmoncel. "I will open it just for you, Madame." When he went behind the counter, I maneuvered her out of earshot.

"I'm Vlad." I took her hand and kissed it gently. "It's a pleasure."

"Misty," she said. "Misty Malone."

She'd probably heard a thousand jerks say, "A beautiful name for a beautiful woman," and I wasn't going down that road. You give a dame like that too much too soon, and before you know it, she moves into your place, dismantles your Heroes of Cheese altar, and clogs your drain with bobby pins.

"So, Misty." I said, "You got plans for the evening?"

"I -"

"You do now," I said. You can't give chicks too much time to think. You have to take control of the situation, tell them what's what. Otherwise they get cagey. "Give me your phone."

She fished her phone out of her giant handbag

and gave it to me. I punched my number into her contacts. "I get off at 9:00. Call me at 9:10 sharp. I'm taking you out."

"Okay." She blushed and patted her hair. "I'm looking forward to it, Vlad."

"Good. Now get out of here. I gotta work."

She skedaddled, and I watched her round little butt sashay in her dress as she walked off. Damn. Garrett emerged with the platter, and I took a handful of Septmoncel. "Too late," I said. "She split."

Back at Coffee Monkey, I negotiated with Nim for the day's tips since I didn't have a dime on me to show Misty a good time. She drove a hard bargain, but we worked it out, and I got enough scratch to take Misty to Lillian's Hometown Grill. Once I dazzled her with my cheese knowledge, she'd be so into me she wouldn't notice that she was eating diner grub.

Misty called at 9:10, and I told her to meet me at Lillian's in twenty minutes. It was just enough time for me to gel my hair and wash my mouth with a Listerine sample I swiped from the mini bin. I looked good. Nim said it was too hot for leather, but I disagreed. My jacket went everywhere with me.

Luckily, I had thrown on my red tee that morning. Red is an aphrodisiac for the ladies. I did a breath check, flicked some dirt off my boots, and headed out.

Misty was there when I arrived, sitting at the counter nursing a milkshake. "I hope you don't mind that I started early," she said. "I was craving ice cream."

I took a deep draw from her straw. Boysenberry. Interesting. I'd have taken her for a cherry vanilla girl. "I love a woman who indulges her appetite," I said.

She ordered onion rings and a flank steak. I got the chicken fried steak and garlic mashed. "So," I said. "What's your thing in life, Misty? What do you do?"

"Dog portraits. But no one wants those since the recession. So I was helping out at my friends' T-shirt shop, but that got slow, too. Now I make jewelry." She reached into her bag and pulled out a string of beads. "I made this. I have an Etsy page."

"Did you make that necklace?" I pointed to her sexy neck.

"Mm-hm." She touched it and smiled. "It was a cinch. But what about you, Vlad? Do you like selling cheese?"

"I don't work at Fabiano's," I said. "Yet."

Her eyes widened. "Why not? You're so knowledgeable!"

The cardinal rule of impressing a lady is to ask her about herself, but something about Misty's deep green eyes and that chiseled bob of hers made me give in and let it all spill. I told her about Garrett Deever, the mozzarella war, the ruined batch of Havarti, and how I got screwed out of a job at Fabiano's. I told her about my ambition to nab that apprenticeship, save up, and open a shop that was so good it would destroy Fabiano's forever. I told her my dream of a farm where I could create my own blue, a blue that would shake the cheese world to its foundations. I told her about the coffee table book I wanted to write, featuring my handmade cheeses. By the time I finished, I had her. She even teared up a little at the part about the farm. When I stopped talking, her mouth was open a little.

"You'll swallow a bee," I said.

She took a swig of her shake. "You're going to get everything you want, Vladimir. I get feelings about things, and I can tell."

Chicks always think they're psychic, but

something about Misty Malone made me believe
her. After dinner, we went for a walk along the pier.
I draped my jacket over her when she shivered, and
felt like a lion when she threw her arm around my
waist to give me a squeeze.

After that, Misty started coming over every night.
It was a lot more fun to make cheese with her
around. The landlord finally replaced the fridge,
so I was able to show her some tricks of the trade.
She was a quick learner and an appreciative eater.
She had instinct. I started sending her to Fabiano's
when Garrett was on shift to flirt with him so
he'd give her samples. It didn't take that brazen
vixen long to start knocking whole wheels of high-
end cheese into her bag as she roped Garrett into
conversations about the subtleties of Broccio versus
Broccio Demi-Affine. She was smooth. Garrett
never saw a thing. For good measure, she'd slip a
few boxes of crackers into her bag on the way out.
Nim would shoplift us some wine (in exchange for
tips), then Misty and I would go back to my place
and have a feast.

Things were good, but after six months, no one
had quit Fabiano's and I was still stuck at Coffee
Monkey. They didn't pay much, and poached

cheese and diner food wasn't going to cut it forever. Reality would set in, and Misty would realize that she was with a broke-ass barista. I talked a good game about the business, but Vlad's Vainglorious Creations hadn't sold a wheel of cheese in months.

One night over champagne and a feast of Emental Grand Cru and strawberries, Misty looked around at my apartment and frowned.

"You need more room if you want to grow the business," she said. "When is Fabiano's going to hire you? We need the money and you need the apprenticeship."

"I'm trying, babe, but those bastards ain't budging. Nim said Whitney's not even taking maternity leave."

Misty's eyes went dark and shifty. She chewed a cracker and dusted her hands off on her dress. "Well, if they're not going on their own, maybe we could... nudge one of them along somehow. Create an opening for you."

"Whoa. I don't know what's on that little mind of yours, but -"

"Oh, I don't mean anything bad! I just mean... let's say someone went away for a little while. Just long enough for you to secure a position. Then that someone could come back. Good as new, no harm, no foul."

I squinted. "What are you suggesting, babe?"

"Nothing! Just that... maybe there's a way we could get someone to disappear. We would hold them for a while. Just until you got their job. And then they could be released. Like a butterfly." I stared at her. In the late evening sun, she was radiant. All of the cheese had filled her out a bit, and her face was soft and round. I would do anything for her, but kidnapping wasn't in my wheelhouse. Besides, pulling off something like that was complicated.

"Of course, we couldn't keep anyone here," she said. "We could use the basement of the tee shirt shop. It's closed for the summer while Jen's in Europe. I still have my key. It's boarded up and Jen won't be back until September."

I'm not one of those candy-asses who gets "anxiety", but I was starting to feel a little edgy. Misty finished her drink and poured herself another. "It would have to look like they left on their own, so we'd need to write a resignation letter. We'd have to plan for family and friends getting suspicious." She furrowed her brow. "Of course, there was that guy you couldn't Google. Adam? Anthony?"

"Antoine," I said. "Antoine Bonnet. I've asked around about him. He lives in a dump over in the Central District. No TV, no internet, can you believe that? He's a shut-in except when he's at Fabiano's. No family. Rumors of a brother in Houston but nothing confirmed."

"Does he have a cat?"

"A cat? What the hell does that matter?"

"If he's locked in the basement, you'll need to feed his cat."

"Dame, I'm telling you right now I ain't feeding no cat. I want an in at Fabiano's, but you're talking about a felony. I'll work shit out in my own time, okay?"

Misty's face suddenly didn't look so soft. She jammed a piece of cheese into her mouth, hoisted her bag onto her shoulder, and snatched the bottle of champagne. "You know, Vlad, I'm beginning to think you don't want to be a better man for me." Then she turned on the waterworks. "I can't keep living on fried chicken and skirt steak. You're wasting your talent and I won't stand around watching while you do it!"

"Come on, baby. You're talking about kidnapping!"

"There's no other way," she hiccupped. "No one's going to leave on their own. And I feel guilty ripping off Garret. He's nice."

At the mention of Garrett, my heart popped like a bad gear. I was gut-slammed by the hellish realization that even Garrett wasn't that stupid. He'd been letting Misty steal. He had it bad for her and this was all of part of some sick master plan to snatch her out from under me. That bastard. I bet he'd been telling her that I was a loser, a dreamer who didn't have the chops to deliver. I wanted to charge over to Fabiano's and break his smug little jaw, but I had a sobbing woman on my hands, and a man has his priorities.

"Garrett's not nice," I told her. "He's hot for that ass of yours. That's why he lets you steal cheese."

Misty folded her arms. "He's a gentlemen, and besides he has a girlfriend!"

I sneered. "Oh, is that what he told you? Sure, he's got a girlfriend. He's got ten. He's a man-whore, Misty. And I told you how he tried to destroy me online! I thought you were on my side!"

Misty was rummaging fiercely in her bag while

I was setting her straight, and she finally found what she was looking for. She held it up to me, her eyes burning. "This is the key to Tees by Jen! on 3rd and Jackson. It opens the back door into the screen print room and the basement. If you ever want to see me again, you will take Antoine, you will stick him in that basement, and you will get his job at Fabiano's." She slapped the key onto the table and marched to the door. "Leave him food and water and don't rough him up. I'm not a monster." She slammed the door, and I was left with nothing but a plate of crumbs and the literal key to my future with Misty Malone.

I remembered seeing Antoine a few weeks ago, subbing for Whitney when she had the pukes. Physically, he was nothing - about 5'7" and a buck forty-five. Mousy hair down to his shoulders, John Lennon glasses, and pasty skin. I'm not one to brag, but the Bardzecki men are muscular guys, and I pump iron, so I was pretty ripped. Physically, this guy wasn't going to be a problem. It was the logistics I had to think through. Misty was better at that stuff than I was, but she was gone, and if I wanted her back I was going to have do the hard thinking myself.

I knew enough about crime to know it was best to keep it simple. You get too elaborate, shit backfires on you real fast. I took my cheese journal from the kitchen, wrote "Kidnapping" and tapped my pen on the page. I'd need some way to get Antoine to the shop basement. I'd have to set a trap; make the prey come to me. I could invite him to pick up some expensive imported stuff, then wrestle him to the floor and lock him up. I'd have to do it without him figuring out who I was, which would mean a disguise. Then there was the resignation letter. I'd have to whip up something plausible and make sure it got delivered to Olin's hands personally. And I didn't know how long I should wait before I threw down for the opening at Fabiano's. Too soon, I'd look like jerk, too late; I'd risk losing it to some upstart, or worse, a crony of Garrett's.

Bottom line: I'd get Antoine to the T-shirt shop under some ruse, lock him up, and bribe Nim to take the forged resignation letter to Olin and tell him Antoine had asked her to drop it off. I'd play it cool for a few days, then sidle up to Olin with a fresh copy of my resume and a sample of my hand-crafted goat cheddar. Then I'd be in. Once I had the position secured, I'd cut Antoine loose. He'd come back with some crazy story of how he'd been kidnapped by a masked man, but everyone would assume he had a psychotic break and was making it up. He'd leave the state, a crushed and broken man. That was a tough break, but in the end, it was for the best.

The next morning I hopped the 43 down to Jackson Street. I got off a few stops ahead of the shop (diverting suspicion) and walked until I found it. Flyers advertising a martial-arts convention were plastered all over the plywood that covered the windows. I walked around back to an scraggly courtyard, tripped on a hoe, and flung that sucker into overgrown grass.

I worked the key in the knob, wrenched the door open, and flipped on the light switch. It was a cramped shop with two dust-covered screen printing machines, a jumble of bulging boxes, and a cash register. It took me a minute to find the stairwell to the basement because it was behind a rack of Tees. The second door at the bottom opened into a basement room with a kitchenette, a bathroom, and a saggy couch.

There were no windows, and I could secure the

door with a padlock. Once I got the locks and chains installed, it would be escape-proof. If Antoine screamed, the noise from the machine shop next door would mask the sound. I tested the faucets and the toilet. Both worked. This would be like a vacation for Antoine. Hell, I was doing the guy a favor.

It was time for a visit to Nim. I hopped the D Line to the Laylor School of the Arts and found her in the dorm parking lot smoking clove cigarettes and playing a round of seven-card stud with some punk poseurs in the back of her Ford pick-up. I swung myself up and told the punks to take a hike. I left Nim with a manila envelope, and, after brutal negotiations, the promise of my first month's pay at Fabiano's. The way I saw it, it was the equivalent of an agency fee. Her delivery was going to get me in the door. Once my career took off, a month's pay wouldn't matter for squat.

The morning of the event, adrenaline was partying in my veins and I was coated in sweat, but I was ready. Like an elite athlete, I had visualized the event over and over until the execution was flawless. I double-checked the items in my duffle bag, and headed to Tees by Jen!

As "Bradford A. Desmond the Third", restaurant tycoon, I had placed an ad on Enzyme, a cheese making message board, offering to sell some top-of-the-line equipment at a quarter of its value because I was delaying the opening of my new eatery due to a bout with throat cancer. Nim figured out Antoine's screen name on Enzyme, and I found out he was in the market for a new cheese press. I put the listing up, Antoine replied in less than an hour, and we set up the meeting. We agreed to meet at 10:00 a.m. sharp, but I planned to get there an hour early to install the lock, get into my ski mask, and do a run through.

When I opened the door to the back of the shop, I started shaking. Usually, criminals start out small - vandalism, or dealing a little pot. I was tackling a felony act right out of the gate. My face broke out into a streaming sweat but I tried to keep my mind on the job.

I stocked the kitchenette with grub, and got to work installing the lock. That's the first thing that went to hell. I'm a crack carpenter on account of the summer I spent helping my uncle install drywall, so I was confident I could knock that job off in twenty minutes tops, but it turns out that shit requires precision. Something went backasswards with the alignment of the plate. When I turned on the Dremel to back out the screws, the power went out. I looked everywhere for the fuse box, but I couldn't find it, so I was stuck with a shitty lock and no power. I had to jerry-rig it with a cheap hasp. When I stress-tested it, it held okay, but fixing it meant a risky extra trip back.

◎

I dug the ski mask out of my bag and pulled it on. I looked menacing as hell in the mirror over the cash register, but I didn't have time to admire myself. It was getting close to ten, and I still had to practice my accent. Bradford A. Desmond the Third had a Scottish brogue. Between the brogue and the hoarseness from throat cancer, he sounded completely unlike me. There's no way Antoine could identify me by voice. I rasped a few "come ins" and "down this ways" to warm up, and did a final sweep to clear out any human detritus a forensics team could catch. It was two minutes to ten.

When the rap at the door came, I was so wound up I almost screamed. "Yes?" called in a raspy brogue. "Who is there?"

"It's Antoine Bonnet? To look at the press?"

"Right. Let yourself in, mate. It's just round the corner down the stairs. Sorry about the lights. I had a wee bit of trouble with me fuse." I crouched, ready to grab his legs so I could swing him down into the basement. My hands were sweat-drenched, and I hoped my gloves would stay on during the fight. Not that I expected much of a contest.

He shuffled around the corner, and as soon as I saw his skinny legs, I dove on him. Then my nose exploded and my left eye burst open. Jesus Christ. The bastard managed to punch the shit out of my face before I could even get a decent grip on him. I almost lost him because I was dazed and half-blinded by the blood, but when he started bucking, adrenaline kicked in and I got focused fast. I had a good foot and half on him, but he was wily as shit, and stronger than he looked. He was close to slipping out of my grasp, but I finally managed to submit him with a right hook to his jaw. I got him in a headlock and dragged him across the threshold. Even with my arms around his neck, he was thrashing like a madman, and I was running out of steam. My mask was sticky with blood. He

reared up and head-butted me in the chin. I bit my
own tongue so hard it started swelling. I slammed
him onto the floor and kicked him in the stomach
hard enough that he was too winded to get up.
I staggered out, yanked the door shut, and was
just getting the padlock snapped down when he
slammed himself against the door. I dropped the
lock twice but finally managed to clamp it shut.
His body slam had splintered the wood. I'd have to
reinforce it when I fixed the lock.

"Hey!" he yelled. "Why are you doing this? You
son of a bitch! You're not going to get any money
for me." He pounded on the door. "Let me out!"

"Ride it out, you pussy. You got snacks and a place
to shit. It's just for a few days."

He body-slammed the door a few more times,
but he was weakening. I'd given him a pretty solid
beat down, even if he did manage to fuck up my
eye. He'd calm down eventually. I treated his water
supply with crushed Valium, courtesy of Nim.

I had timed this operation to coincide with my
days off. Bags of frozen peas took the bruising
down a bit, but it was still ugly. And it was
killing me not to have the scoop on Fabiano's. I'd
instructed Nim to drop off the resignation letter the

morning of the kidnapping, so they had two full days to get used to the idea, but they were a tight-knit group, and this was going to cause some buzz. That's when I'd swoop in with a clean copy of my resume and save the day.

When I got back to work, Nim laughed and asked how the other guy looked. She didn't want to know anything about the cloak-and-dagger shit with the letter and the Valium, but she was smart enough to comprehend it wasn't strictly above board.

When I glanced at Fabiano's, I saw Garrett with his head down, talking to Whitney and Ansel. They looked glum. I ambled over. "I hear you got a new shipment of Dunsyre coming from Scotland this week."

Whitney frowned and Garrett shook his head. "Perhaps next month. It needs more time in the cave."

"Jesus, buck up. What's a month's wait?"

"It's not that," Whitney said. "Things have been weird since Antoine left."

"He didn't even say goodbye," said Ansel.

"He did not want a big fuss and sadness," Garrett told him. "He is a shy man."

I stifled a snort. "Whoa." I said, "You mean he just

quit?"

Garrett nodded. "He asked Nim to give a letter to Olin. He said -"

"He said that he needed to leave town for a while and figure out his life." Said Whitney, narrowing her eyes. "That's not like him. His dojo is here. His friends are here. He -"

"His dojo?"

"He was earning a blue belt," said Garrett. "He had many friends."

So that's how he fucked up my face.

"Shit. That's tough. Now you gotta train somebody new, huh?"

Whitney rolled her eyes. "Real subtle, Vlad. Olin's not even going to look at resumes until the quarterly reports are in, so don't reach for his fly just yet." She grabbed a wheel of Livarot and stomped off.

"When is he going to have those numbers?" I asked Garrett.

He shrugged. "Soon." He leaned in to me and lowered his voice. "I promise I will tell you the instant I hear."

I narrowed my eyes. "He's not planning to give the job to one of your punk relatives, is he?"

Garrett looked hurt. "Olin does not believe in such ways."

Yet another delay to the start of my career. In the meantime, that lock needed to be fixed before Antoine decided to karate chop the door down. The next morning I headed over to Tees by Jen! with a stronger hasp and a new lock. As soon as I opened the back door, Antoine started moaning and thumping at the inner door. I slipped on my ski mask just in case.

"Shut up," I said. "You're fine. Do me a wee favor. Look round the room for a fuse box. I need to tighten the screws on this plate."

"Are you kidding me?"

"Come on, bloke. It's only for a few more days."

"Fuck off. By the way, this food is processed garbage."

"Look for that fuse box or I'm going to come in there with restraints and you ain't gonna like it."

"Good luck, asshole. You forgot a little something when you prepped this guest room. You come in after me, you're gonna get cut."

I hoped he was bluffing, but just in case, I needed something for protection. I headed out for the hoe I'd thrown into courtyard. A blow to the head would shut him up for a while. As I pushed the outer door open, I felt resistance, then my nose exploded for the second time in a week. A knee rammed into my gut so hard I almost puked. I heard a crack and felt a searing pain my left ribcage. I couldn't breathe because my neck was being squeezed. I felt like I going to pass out when I heard another crack. Somehow my mask had come off and my forehead had been slammed into the door jamb. More blood. My stomach was still balled up from the kick and I couldn't seem to get any leverage. I was seeing double and dry-heaving. Zip ties were jerked onto my wrists.

"In here!" Antoine yelled, pounding the door. My assailant stomped his foot on my back, pushing my chin into the floor, then yanked me inside and flipped me over onto my back. He stuck his beefy face in mine and spat on me. "Stay here," he said. With three kicks, he broke the basement door down, and Antoine staggered out.

"Antoine, you okay, buddy? He hurt you?"

"I'm okay, Tom. How did you find me?"

"Story for another time, man. Mom's been worried sick."

Shit. So the brother in Houston was real. I tried to

talk but I coughed up a sheet of blood instead.

Antoine's brother grabbed me by the neck, flung me forward, and cut the zip ties. "I called the cops while I was outside, so there's no sense in running."

Antoine stared at me. "What the fuck, man! You're that barista dude who's always hanging around Fabiano's, aren't you?"

"That's just a temp job," I gasped, "until Fabiano's hires me."

Antoine smirked. "They're not going to hire you. Olin promised any new openings to Garrett's cousin from Ohio."

A swell of rage and adrenaline exploded through me, and the pain faded. All I could think about was ruining Garrett Deever's face, Garrett Deever, who took everything from me. Garrett Deever, who didn't deserve his life. Garrett Deever, who had backstabbed me for the last time. I heard myself scream, a roar of anguish and wrath, and my body was moving, kicking Antoine and Tom as they tried to grab me. I was a dervish, an animal. I fled, powered with the mania of a man who'd felt the bite of injustice one too many times. Blood flew from my face and I was half-blind, but I was possessed. I ran for Misty and for our life together.

I ran for the goddamned respect I was owed. I ran for good-quality Swiss. By the time I got to the door of Mac's Famous Food Mart, my chest was on fire and I was limping, but my rage boiled over.

As I staggered towards the kiosk, Garrett Deever was tying the Fabiano's apron strings on a younger, blonder version of himself. He heard the cop's shouts and turned his head towards me. He looked surprised as hell, but not as surprised as he was going to be. I leaped over the display, grabbed him by the throat, and drew back my hand back. The fact that that punch never landed is my biggest regret. Instead, my arm got yanked back so hard it popped, then the ceiling dropped on me and I was out.

My ribs still hurt sometimes and my nose never straightened out, even with the finest medical care in our state prison where I sit, cellmates with a schizophrenic who thinks Velveeta is the king of cheeses. I've tried to educate him, but there's only so much learning a 300-pound serial arsonist is open to. They got me for kidnapping, possession of stolen property, criminal trespassing, assault and forgery. The forgery charge was courtesy of Nim, who ratted me out when they threatened to name her as an accomplice. The whole thing went sideways in the first place because Antoine's brother, a detective in Houston, was in town for the martial arts convention. When Antoine didn't show up for his dojo's exhibition match, Tom got suspicious and talked to Olin. Once he saw the resignation letter, he put the pieces together pretty fast.

I got a job in the prison kitchen and eventually worked my way up from the slop line to manager, but I don't have any say over the food. We're locked into a contract with a national chain, and I can't get so much as a wedge of low-end Brie in here. I refuse to call orange squares of pressed chemical powder "cheese". But what doesn't kill a man makes him stronger. Every time one of those monstrosities gets slapped onto a piece of bread, it just makes me more determined to get what's mine.

Misty visits twice a week. She got in good with one of the guards and smuggles me in something nice when she can. Last week, it was Brebis du Lavort. She says none of the original crew has quit Fabiano's, but that's nothing to me now since those bastards blacklisted me. Nim dropped out of art school to manage Coffee Monkey. Antoine made black belt and won a couple of big fights. Misty says he's socking away his winnings to open his own shop. Garrett the Weasel King managed to talk Whitney into marrying him, and he's raising her kid as his own now. Antoine's kidnapping made national news, and with all the publicity (How Far Would You Go to Get Your Dream Job?), Fabiano's expanded. They also beefed up their apprenticeship program, and Garrett's cousin got in. I've got Misty doing damage control on my blog, but she says I don't have a chance in hell of getting my reputation back any time soon. Everyone took Antoine's side, thanks to Garrett Deever and his fake moral outrage.

It doesn't matter. I'll be out one day, and when Vlad Bardzecki the Second unleashes his greatness upon the cheese world, Garrett Deever better blow town, because I'm coming for him. I'm coming for the entire artisan cheese world, and they'd better prepare for a reckoning.

DISOBEY ME

by Sally Gardner

They told me I was dyslexic
it didn't describe me
belonged in the library
of words I can't spell
no matter how many times they tell
you just try harder sound it out
simple when you think about
it. Stop giving me the third degree
don't put me down
don't make me fret
I can't learn my alphabet
it doesn't go in any logical order
the stress gives me attention deficit disorder
at school I wanted to go it alone
they told me that's unwise
they called me unteachable
I was unreachable
stuck in the classroom,
broken by rules
by buttons and ties.

But I don't like the little words they always disobey
me
the does doses up and is higher than a dude should
be

So they tested me
they corrected me
and found my results poor
and told me I wasn't concentrating
they expected more.
I tried to get along
I never made the score

And I think about Chaucer in those freedom days
when no one found your spelling faulty for the
extra Es and As
Mr Shakespeare I wonder would they let him write
his plays?
Oh woe is me
might just be
graffti in a bog
And Hamlet the name
he called his prize-fighter dog

But I don't like the little words they always disobey

me
the doe doses dope and is higher than a do should
be

You say that you're a writer
but that's absurd
how do you write
if you cannot spell the words?
listen, it's not the way I spell
that makes me want to write
It's the way I see the world
That makes me want to fight
I challenge you – see the words as I do
feel them sting your skin
the meaning often shocking
the way the nib goes in
to relish discombobulate not to moderate your
passion
not to murder language in an artificial fashion
words are our servants
we are not their slaves
it matters not if we spell them wrong it matters
what they say

But I don't like the little words they always disobey

me
the does doses dope and is higher than a dough
should be.

AFTERWORD AFTERWARD

In ode to Louise Tondeur's emotive *Foreward Foreword* i'm calling this an *Afterword Afterward*, and if you asked me later which was the correct spelling, I couldn't tell you.

In the creation, and development of this manuscript I've found that it is not spelling, grammar, or lack thereof, which connects these pieces. The linchpin was not missing pronouns, malapropisms, or any of these spices of language which are synecdochic.

To find the unifying concept, I had to refer back to a recommendation that I was once given by a very imaginative dyslexic friend, Jon Arden, who taught me that the creative process involves letting go of words:

> Look at all the issues involved, try to visualize them not as separate or static, imagine them as changing parts with in a bigger system. Try to find a calm place in your mind and let an image of all the separate parts interacting as a whole come to your mind don't worry about feeling you are missing all the facts if there are holes in the metal model just glide over them for now. Once you feel you have a working sense of the whole system or problem, let go of if and see what ideas present them selves to you.

Despite this advice there were themes, individual items, that my mind wanted to hold onto: Louise

Tondeur's tree growing wool, Matthew Scurfield's play, that bought him to question the nature of authority, and why some people have it and other don't. An idea that echoed into Sally Gardner's 'flip flop' poem, which talks of spelling errors in the great writers and the significance of ideas and passion to writing.

It is of course, a great honour to have a piece included in the anthology by Sally Gardner. A prolific writer, who is doing a wonderful job on re-educating the world about dyslexia. Likewise, Rebecca Loncraine, whose writing and perspective on dyslexia has shaped my own understanding. From whose piece *Everything is Spherical*, the anthology takes its name.

There are, I should note, a number of pieces included in this anthology which refer to a body of work outside, such as Ross Cooper's piece *Dysobedience*, I encourage you to look up (search for Ross Cooper's *Social Model of Dyslexia*).

It is nearly a decade ago when I first stumbled into Ross's office trying, and failing, to explain my theory that dyslexic writing or poetics was, like surrealism, made up of its own code only decipherable by those who are dyslexic.

I have learnt since, while dyslexic writers may come from shared experience - one which infuses the opening of this anthology - the doors, tunnels and channels the writers have traversed, both in and outside their imagination, complicate the very notion of *dyslexia*.

The paradox of a dyslexic writer, it turns out, is not that they can write but the term *dyslexia* fails to tell the complete story. So while I imagined I would, as a dyslexic reader/editor be able to instantly relate to all dyslexic writers, and identify with/ transcribe all *dyslexic poetics*, this just isn't true.

Editing has involved trying to get a global aesthetic. Like a hairdresser, i've been snipping off edges that hang loose. It's a visual-pattern thing that I struggle to articulate into anything reasonably lateral-cohesive. Perhaps because of this, I've found I've been seen by some authors as an evil witch teacher from the author's past, correcting them. As if I'm telling them they are wrong; rejecting them all over again.

Dyslexics are right to be angry about being let down by their education and those wasted years, as Louise Tondeur said at the start. But I wonder if to be a writer, it is also necessary to not conflate those teachers, who shamed, humiliated, and patronised, with constructive critics, for new stories to emerge.

These do not have to be cohesive, linear or grammatical, because writing ought only show how we love the words which we mislaid, as we tried to corral them. To offer another *perception.*

Making the image of this book *a looking glass,* or a mirror into a world seen beyond. Serving both as a reference to the late dyslexic writer Lewis Carroll and representing a different lens for seeing and storytelling.

ACKNOWLEDGEMENTS

Thanks goes to POET whose sponsorship made this publication possible. And to Matthew Scurfield, for introducing me to POET, as well as offering his ongoing support and commitment to RASP. Your kind, strong words are wonderful. Thanks also goes to Sarah Fearn, Caroline Gardner and Louise Tondeur who have each played instrumental roles in the development of the anthology at its various stages. Another big thanks goes to Lucie Cooper my design guru, who I can never thank enough for sharing her wonderful thoughts and ideas for free. You are the best.

Thanks also to my original teacher, and harshest critic, Tom. And my family; my generous husband, my sweet baby daughter, my parents – especially the dyslexic one - and of course, my mother-in-law, looking after my baby right now as I type. Thank-you all.

ABOUT THE AUTHORS

Ross Cooper was born in London rain and grew up under African sun. Despite an unpromising educational start, he survived the trauma of schooling, finding education much more interesting at postgraduate level where he was allowed more freedom to dream. He has been writing songs and academic stories, including developing the social model of dyslexia, working as an innovative educationalist and sculpting visual ideas ever since. He is also the originator of the Festival of Dyslexic Culture.

Annelise Evans graduated with a degree in philosophy from Cardiff University in 2005. She is currently studying for a Master's in Education and hopes to teach others who have specific learning difficulties. This is her first publication.

Nicky Fawley has always loved writing, but found school difficult. She returned to study as a mature student in 2010 and completed an Arts and

Humanities Access course before being offered a place to study Creative Writing at Roehampton University. Nicky is currently finishing her degree part time via the Open University. This will be her first published piece of work.

Fernando A Flores was born in Reynosa, Tamaulipas, Mexico. His poetry has appeared most recently in *Bat City Review*, among others. He is the author of *Death to the Bullshit Artists of South Texas, Vol.1* (CCLaP 2014), and is the recipient of the 2014 Cisneros del Moral Honorable Mention Award. He lives in central Texas.

Sally Gardner is a multi-award-winning novelist whose work has been translated into more than twenty-two languages. Her novel MAGGOT MOON (Hot Key Books) won both the Costa Children's Book Prize and the Carnegie Medal 2013.

Robert Glück is a poet, fiction writer, and editor. He earned an MA at San Francisco State University and co-founded the New Narrative movement in San Francisco in the early 1980s. He is the author of nine books, including two novels, *Margery Kempe* and *Jack the Modernist,* and a book of stories, *Denny Smith.* He is a professor of creative writing at San Francisco State University.

Dee Kirkby is the Patron of Reading at Beacon View Primary Academy and was the 2012 Writer in Residence for Portsmouth Libraries. she is the author of *Without Alice, My Dream of You, Realand, Raffie Island* and *Queendom* (The Portal Series for children), *Special Deliveries: Life Changing Moments* and *My Mini Midwife.*

Rebeeca Loncraine went to art school for a year, left for university with a passion for literature, and eventually gained a doctorate in English Literature from Oxford University. Her first book was *The Real Wizard of Oz: The Life and Times of L. Frank Baum* (Gotham, Penguin USA, 2009). She is now writing a book about flight and the human imagination, entitled *Skybound,* to be published by Picador in 2016.

Kristen McHenry is a poet and fiction writer who lives and works in Seattle. Her work has been seen in publications including *Busk, Tiferet, Big Pulp, Dark Matter,* and the anthology, *Many Trails to the Summit.* Her chapbook *The Goatfish Alphabet* was runner-up in qarrtsiluni's 2009 chapbook contest, and was published by Naissance Press in April of 2010. Her second chapbook, *Triplicity: Poems in Threes* was published by Indigo Ink Press in 2011, and a pairing of her short stories was published under the title of *Tender Vessels* in 2013 by Loyal Stone Press. She is also the author of *The Acme Employee Handbook* published by Jaffa Press in early 2014. She loves to sing, but only in the car with all of the windows rolled up.

Alex Nile is dyslexic, a SEN/Dyslexia-specialist Teacher (now Head of Learning Support at a Public school in North London), and the author of three fiction books based on dyslexic themes, specialising in the emotional coping that many dyslexics encounter: *SCHOOL: The Ultimate Dyslexic Battleground* (a primary school-based novel), *The Deceitful Dyslexic* (a young adult novel), and *The Dyslexic Virus: Turning the World Dyslexic.* You can find more information about his work at dyslexia-research.com.

Matthew Scurfield has worked on many different theatre projects in the UK - traversing the far corners of the stage, from Dundee to Cornwall, from the pantheons of Berkoff"s London theatre Group, to Shakespeare's New Globe, The Royal National Theatre and a lengthy adventure with ground-breaking *Complicite*. He has appeared in numerous films and television productions. Despite, or perhaps because of, being severely dyslexic Matthew published two books, I *Could be Anyone* and *Off The Line.*

Ruth Solomon studied Social Anthropology at a University and later began working in the heady atmosphere of Special Needs Adult Education. She has published various pieces of writing in magazines- many of them on-line- and exhibited her art work locally from time to time. Later she qualified as a Shiatsu Practitioner and began working as a Therapist mainly with Autisitc and non-verbal children. She set up a Garden Arts Project "Memory Gardens" for adults and children on the Autistic Spectrum and for people with mental health pressures.

Elizabeth Tasker is an astrophysicist working in Japan. She won the 'Leap Local Travel Writing Competition' for describing Japanese toilets in unflushable detail. A number of her science articles have also received acclaim, including second prize in the 2014 'Chemistry World Science Communication Competition', first prize in category for the 2013 'Global Voices from Japan' column contest and first prize in the 1999 'Daily Telegraph Young Science Writers Awards'. Her blog can be found at girlandkat.com.

AJ Thatcher holds an MPhil from Exeter and an MA from Goldsmiths'. In 2012 he published *Teaching Creative Writing*. He's currently working as an online English tutor, teacher trainer for EFL English teachers and is about to start studying to be a dyslexia support worker for university students.

Louise Tondeur's first two novels *The Water's Edge* (2003) and *The Haven Home for Delinquent Girls* (2004) were published by Headline Review. Her most recent publications are *You are not Special* in Litro Magazine (2014), 'The Swim' in *The Front View* (2013) and a poem called 'Voices' in *Forgotten*

Letters: An Anthology of Dyslexic Literature (2011). She also contributed 'Versions of Creative Writing Teaching' to *Writing in Education* (Spring 2014). Louise teaches Creative Writing at the University of Roehampton. You'll find her website at louisetondeur.co.uk

Lennie Varvarides has produced the dyspla festival since 2007, the first arts organisation to stage the work of dyslexic story makers. In 2013 dyspla became an arts council England recognised organisation and strives to challenge dyslexic narrative. www.dyspla.com

Jacs Vittles story *Dyslexia – An Amazing Discovery* was published in March 2010. Following various honourable mentions in short story competitions, Jacqui is now beavering away at what she plans to be a murder mystery series and has other draft manuscripts waiting for their turn in the limelight. She lives in Sydney, Australia.

Aby Watson is a performance maker and artist based in Glasgow. Her work spans both solo and collaborative practice, creating new pieces of contemporary performance that play with movement, choreography, text, action and autobiography. Her writing explores the relationship between specific learning differences and artistic practices. Her book *Dyslexia, Writing and Performance* was published by RASP in 2013.

Eric R. Williams is an American author living in Oslo Norway. His works include three novels, numberous magazine articles, poetry and short stories. He has created an award winning TV show about genealogy in Norway.

Lightning Source UK Ltd.
Milton Keynes UK
UKOW05f1307301014

240827UK00002B/31/P